“You

“I knew that when I

That’s why I chose y

They didn’t have what you have.”

“What—exactly—do I have, Mr. Blake?” she purred provocatively.

“You don’t need me to put it into words,” he said coolly.

She gave him her most wide-eyed innocent stare, and her voice hovered on the edge of a chuckle. “Oh, but I’d like to know what name you’d put to it.”

It was on the tip of his tongue to say bluntly that she was a sexy little number, but the words wouldn’t form themselves, and what came out was quite different.

“God help the man who’s fool enough to fall in love with you,” he said abruptly. “You could give him heaven or hell.”

Dear Reader:

SILHOUETTE DESIRE is an exciting new line of contemporary romances from Silhouette Books. During the past year, many Silhouette readers have written in telling us what other types of stories they'd like to read from Silhouette, and we've kept these comments and suggestions in mind in developing SILHOUETTE DESIRE.

DESIREs feature all of the elements you like to see in a romance, plus a more sensual, provocative story. So if you want to experience all the excitement, passion and joy of falling in love, then SILHOUETTE DESIRE is for you.

For more details write to:

LUCY GORDON

My Only Love, My Only Hate

Silhouette Desire

Originally Published by Silhouette Books
division of
Harlequin Enterprises Ltd.

First published in Great Britain in 1987
by Silhouette Books, 15–16 Brook's Mews, London W1A 1DR

ISBN 0 373 50576 0

22–0487

Printed and bound in Great Britain by
Cox & Wyman Ltd, Reading

To Linda – with thanks for more than I can say.

LUCY GORDON

lives in Venice, Italy, with her Italian husband and three cats. For twelve years she was a writer on an English women's magazine but left to be a full-time novelist. When not writing, she likes to travel extensively and go to the theater as much as possible.

Other Silhouette Books by Lucy Gordon

Silhouette Special Edition

Legacy of Fire
Enchantment in Venice

Silhouette Desire

Take All Myself
The Judgement of Paris
A Coldhearted Man

My only love sprung from my only hate,
Too early seen unknown, and known too late!
Prodigious birth of love it is to me,
That I must love a loathed enemy.

Romeo and Juliet
Act I, Scene IV
William Shakespeare

Prologue

There was a stir in London's Central Criminal Court when the counsel for the prosecution made his entrance. Young, handsomc and severe, Giles Blake had the assurance that goes with natural authority. He would have caused heads to turn under any circumstances.

But today the circumstances were exceptional. This was his day of glory, the day he would bring to a triumphant conclusion his prosecution of the crooked financier Andrew Haines on charges of fraud and embezzlement. As he entered the court, those in the public gallery strained forward to get a better look at his tall dark figure, for already he carried the aura of success that sets a man apart. Even some of the battered veterans of the legal profession, cynical men who'd seen it all, stopped for a moment, conscious that a young lion had come among them.

He was twenty-eight, too young, some had said, to undertake the major task of prosecuting Andrew Haines. But all doubts had been stilled by the masterly way he'd handled his case. No one could forget the biting savagery with which he'd cross-examined Haines himself.

With Haines's daughter, Tanis, he'd been more restrained, questioning her with chill courtesy. That was a good move, the veterans agreed among themselves. The girl was only eighteen and it would have been a mistake to attack her too cruelly and rouse the jury's sympathy. Slender, blond and white-faced, she'd stood immobile in the dock. Only her eyes, burning with hate for her interrogator, had seemed alive.

Despite his careful courtesy, Giles Blake's contempt for Tanis had been obvious. In private his colleagues had heard him mutter, "spoiled rich brat," and certainly something in her fragile beauty had seemed to bring out the worst in him. Coldly, inexorably, he'd lured her down one confusing path after another, allowing her to tie herself in knots, until at last he elicited the damaging admission he'd been waiting for. Her face had gone the color of death as she realized what she'd said and how it could rebound against her father. It had been too late then for her frantic explanations. Giles Blake had coldly snapped, "No further questions!"

Just before taking his seat, Giles cast a brief glance up at the public gallery. There sat his wife, Belinda, as he'd known she would be. She was eight months pregnant and the gallery was an uncomfortable place to be, but nothing would have her miss her husband's triumph.

Belinda's father was a judge, and she was used to living at the top of the legal tree. There had been a few eyebrows raised at her marriage to Giles Blake, a self-made man from a rough background so different from her own; a man who had pulled himself up by his bootstraps, and whose consuming ambition was just a little too blatant for comfort. But it was becoming clear that her judgment hadn't been at fault. Wherever Giles had started, he was headed for the top, and this trial would help to take him there.

For a moment, as he looked at Belinda, a brief smile relaxed the severity of Giles's features. He was about to turn away but halted suddenly as if a hand had stayed him. Almost unwillingly his eyes rested on the young woman sitting immediately behind Belinda. He knew the pale, delicate face, the blond hair and the huge dark eyes. He'd seen them clearly enough in the witness box as he'd led her into a minefield and made her damn her father. He'd seen the loathing written starkly on her features, and he'd accepted it as a natural part of his job.

But now there was something else in those eyes. Even at this distance their scorn seemed to reach out and touch him. Tanis Haines despised him. It was unbelievable, but true. All her life she'd been her father's spoiled darling, a beautiful, useless creature, living on his ill-gotten gains, good for nothing but to wear the luxurious clothes he bought her. Right now she wore on her back a mink coat that would once have paid Giles's food and rent for a year. And she despised him.

He turned away abruptly, conscious that people were staring at him with curiosity. But the moment had given him a disagreeable sensation that left him briefly unsettled. Then he put it firmly aside.

Andrew Haines was being brought into court now. He was a huge bear of a man, with white hair and a magnificent head. His months in prison had left him pale and taken some of the flesh from him. But he was still a handsome man with a cultivated air. His eyes immediately went to his daughter. Against his will Giles followed that gaze and was shaken by what he saw.

Tanis Haines gazed down at her father with such naked, blazing love that Giles almost wanted to turn away. But stronger still was the impulse to look at her and see how her love transformed her heart-shaped face. She smiled at her father in a pathetic attempt at reassurance, and he smiled back. Giles knew a feeling of disturbance. Such raw emotion, cutting across the boundaries of guilt and innocence, had no place in these grave proceedings. Haines was a criminal. His daughter was, at best, a bit of artful confectionary, at worst, an accomplice in his guilt. Yet their love glowed in the grim courtroom, casting sober, law-abiding citizens in the shade.

A stir announced the judge's arrival. Giles hastily tore his eyes away. His moment had come, and he could allow himself no distractions now. He waited calmly while the formalities were dispensed with, then, taking a deep breath, he began his summing up.

"Ladies and gentlemen of the jury, you have before you an unenviable task. At first glance this case appears to be one of extraordinary complexity. My learned friend for the defense has sought to blind us all with figures, and some of us may feel that he has succeeded. I know he's certainly confused me."

From the body of the court there was light laughter and a perceptible air of settling back to enjoy the performance of a master. The defense counsel looked glum. He knew he was in for a bad time.

Giles continued smoothly, "This complexity is merely an illusion. The truth is actually very simple. Andrew Haines, over a period of years, deliberately and systematically defrauded the companies he controlled until some of them drifted to actual bankruptcy...."

His voice was a marvelous instrument for making a speech: a rich, resonant bass that reached every corner of the courtroom, and that made the most ordinary statements sound impressive.

"He had a network of bank accounts in this country and abroad, hoping by this means to cover his tracks. For a time he succeeded. But when that network began to unravel, it transpired that ultimately the lines all led back to one man, and that man was Andrew Haines."

Out of the corner of his eye Giles could see that Haines himself appeared not to be listening to him. His eyes were fixed on his daughter, high in the public gallery. Giles fought the temptation to glance upward to see if she was looking back.

"He accumulated vast amounts of money, amounts that you and I can only dream of, all for the private profit of one man—Andrew Haines."

He led them easily through the maze of financial transactions, simplifying the complex. His tone was one of light irony.

"Mr. Haines has maintained that this was a normal procedure. Perhaps it is. I don't know. I am not a financier. But when I consider a world in which such betrayal of trust is 'normal prodecure,' I can only say that I am glad I am not."

In the public gallery, Tanis Haines forced herself to be still and silent. But out of sight her nails dug into her palm as though she were rending the hated face of the prosecutor.

Having dealt with the financial evidence, Giles Blake moved smoothly on to discuss his cross-examination of Tanis. His tone had the same chill courtesy as before, but the note of irony had become more biting.

"You may wish to take Miss Haines's assertions at their face value, or you may think it unlikely that . . ."

Heads turned toward the white-faced girl sitting motionless in the gallery. She stared down, her eyes fixed on her father.

"For much of her life, Miss Haines has had no mother and her devotion to her father is evident. She has stated under oath that there is nothing they wouldn't do for each other. What does 'nothing' include? Perjury? When Miss Haines suggests that the discovery of certain forged documents came 'like a bolt from the blue' to her father, is she protecting him? Or is it more likely that Andrew Haines lied to his daughter the way he lied to his colleagues, to his creditors, to the people who trusted him . . ."

"You smug, self-satisfied bastard!"

The cry rang through the court, and at once all heads turned to Tanis Haines in the gallery. She'd risen and was standing at the front of the gallery, clutching the rail and shrieking her hatred to Giles Blake. Tears were pouring down her face.

"You don't care what happens to anyone as long as you make your lousy money! You'll destroy us and forget us because people are nothing to you. . . ."

The court ushers had descended on her, seizing her arms, trying to remove her. But, demented with rage and grief, she managed to escape them and come back to the rail. Giles Blake hadn't moved all this time. He stood like a man of stone, his gaze fixed on her, his eyes burning as he faced his accuser.

"But *I* won't forget *you*!" she cried to him. "One day I'll come back and make you wish you hadn't done it, I swear I will. . . ."

The ushers had taken firmer hold of her and were dragging her away. Her voice blurred into sobs, and finally even they were silenced as the doors were closed behind her.

The judge cleared his throat uncomfortably.

"Most unfortunate and distressing," he murmured. "Mr. Blake, would you like a brief adjournment?"

Giles made no reply. He remained frozen, his eyes turned toward that empty place at the rail, as though he could still see the girl standing there, hurling her contempt at him. He seemed oblivious to everything around him.

"Mr. Blake—" repeated the judge.

With an almost visible effort, Giles became aware of his surroundings. He looked disoriented, like a man who had returned from another world.

"I beg Your Lordship's pardon," he said formally.

"Do you wish for a brief adjournment?"

Suddenly Giles pulled himself together. His voice became crisp and confident again. Only his pallor betrayed that anything had happened.

"Thank you, My Lord, but I am quite ready to continue. I should like to draw the jury's attention to..."

In seconds, it seemed, the court was his again. He dominated it effortlessly with the beauty of his voice and the lucidity of his arguments. Everyone relaxed. Giles Blake was a tough professional, and it would take more than this to put him off.

After Giles's masterful summing up, the defense counsel did the best he could, but everyone knew it was useless. Andrew Haines was found guilty on all counts and sentenced to ten years in jail. It was said afterward that Blake's brilliant performance had added a good two years to the sentence.

But Andrew Haines never served his full sentence. After three months in prison he died of a heart attack.

One

The rain pelted down unceasingly. It caught on Rae Bonham's collar as she stood at the bus stop, and when she got on the bus it dribbled down her neck, so that a chill damp spread through her clothes.

The bus moved at a crawl, impeded by snarled traffic. Rae hung determinedly on to the strap, bracing her body against the sway of the vehicle, waiting, eyes closed, for the interminable journey to end. Her stop was the last one on the route. She reached it half an hour late and began the long, cold walk to the Spartan apartment block where she lived. She tried to hurry. She had a lot to do before she was ready to go out.

The elevator had broken down yet again. Wearily she climbed the four flights of stairs, ignoring the graffiti on the walls. She knew it all by heart.

The apartment was small and shabby but spotlessly clean. Every item of the sparse furniture had been bought second-hand and was carefully arranged so the most worn places of the carpet were almost hidden. Rae hated the place, but it was all she could afford.

By day she worked in a dead-end job as a secretary in a small building firm. Most of her evenings were spent studying for an economics degree. In a few months she was due to take her final exams, a date that was marked in red on her calendar. That, she promised herself, would be the end of the dark days. Till then she had to just hang on.

Even with the apartment's moderate rent Rae couldn't have survived on her tiny salary without some other source of income. She provided it by keeping her name on the books at an escort agency, and working one evening a week.

"Working" meant spending a few hours in public with a man she'd never met before, pretending to be his girlfriend. She was a glamorous accessory for men who were too dull, too busy or too shy to acquire one in the normal manner. Tonight she'd have liked nothing better than to stay home quietly with her books. But halfway through the afternoon she'd had a call from Sally, the young woman who ran the agency.

"I've got a rush job," she said. "A man came in at lunchtime and wants a 'girlfriend' for tonight. It sounds like a good evening. There'll be dinner and dance at a five-star hotel. Lots of champagne, very dressy. Wear your glad rags."

"Sally, isn's there anyone else who could go?" Rae asked.

"Sorry, sweetie—it has to be you. He wants someone madly glamorous."

"I'm not madly glamorous."

"You are in that red wig. I showed him a picture of you wearing it, and he said 'That's the one I want.' You'll get a good meal, anyway."

"That's something, I suppose," said Rae, thinking of the cheese sandwich she'd had for lunch. "What's he like?"

"Youngish, nice-looking, a bit lofty. I got the feeling he'd never been to an agency before and didn't like finding himself in one—know what I mean?"

"All right, I'll do it. Let's have the details."

"His name's Giles Blake. He said he'd collect you in his car but I told him you don't allow that, so you're to be at his place by eight o'clock. Have you got a pencil to take down the address? Rae? Rae, are you still there?"

"Yes, I'm here. What did you say his name was?"

"Blake. Giles Blake. What's the matter, sweetie? You sound funny. Not sick, are you?"

"No," said Rae blankly. Then she pulled herself together. There was no way she could tell Sally why the name Giles Blake had seemed to stab her. "Will you give me that address again?"

All the way home, the name thrummed through her head. She found herself compulsively computing the odds in a brain that was naturally agile with figures. Giles was a common enough name and there must be several hundred Blakes in London alone. The chances of it being *that* Giles Blake were slim.

In the apartment, she studied her face, trying to see in it the eager, happy girl she'd once been. She could find no trace of her. That had been another life, a life that had ended eight years ago when the police had knocked on the door and invited her father to "discuss certain matters."

Hardship and misery had left their mark on her. Few people now would recognize "Rae Bonham" as Tanis Haines, the spoiled darling whose father had indulged her with every luxury. But she was still lovely.

From her tall, elegant mother Rae had inherited her height and slender curvaceous body. She had her mother's heart-shaped face, too, and the delicate bone structure that would make her beautiful all her life. But curiously blended with this were the blunter features of her stocky father. She had his mouth—wide and generous and made for laughter. But whereas Andrew had seemed to be always laughing, Rae's mouth was too often set in a tense line these days.

Her eyes were large and deep blue, fringed with dark, curling lashes. They were slightly wide apart, which could give her a look of breathless naïveté completely at variance with her true character. Her father's eyes had been the same, and his look of childlike wonder had been one of his strongest assets in dealing with business rivals who had habitually underestimated him.

She threw off her damp clothes and showered in the cramped bathroom. When she'd dried herself, she pulled open the door of her wardrobe and took out two garments that were startlingly out of place in these dreary surroundings.

One was a dress in soft, clinging material that appeared to be gold, faintly shot through with black. It had cost her the earnings from her first three evenings' work, but she'd never regretted the investment. The dress was a suitable costume for the role she had to play. It had a blatant, overstated glamour that pleased the men who hired her company. For them she was the embodiment of a fantasy, in which subtlety had no place.

The other garment was a mink jacket of a gleaming, perfect beauty. In that bleak apartment it glowed like a pearl set in iron. Rae's face softened as she ran her hand over its silky sheen. It had been her father's last gift to her, and she would beg in the streets before she sold it.

Everything else that belonged to Tanis Haines had gone, even her name. The horrific blaze of publicity that surrounded her father's trial and death had left her with a desperate longing to vanish from the world's sight. She'd adopted not only her mother's maiden name, but her Christian name, too.

Andrew had believed himself to be beyond the reach of the law, so he'd never thought to make provision for her. After his death, every penny he'd owned was tied up in bankruptcy proceedings. Tanis had managed to salvage only her moveable possessions.

These had been considerable, and at first she hadn't felt the pinch of poverty. But it wasn't long before she'd begun to realize that her upbringing had left her vulnerable. Her mother was dead and she was an only child. Her father had reared her to be a companion to him—beautiful, charming, but basically useless.

Flung unexpectedly into a hostile world, she'd soon understood the disadvantages of having no training or qualifications. She'd begun to sell her jewelry, receiving much less for it than it was worth and spending the proceeds far too quickly because she knew only how to live luxuriously.

After the jewelry she'd started to sell the furs, and gradually she'd begun to panic. She had nothing to live on and no way of earning a living. Shock had forced her to pull herself together.

She'd studied shorthand and typing while she lived on the last of her money. She had finally become reasonably proficient, but she knew she'd never be more than that.

She'd obtained a job with Kinroy & Son, a small firm of builders whose owner didn't mind her slow speed. He had known she was the best he'd ever get for the scandalously low money he offered. Rae had earlier applied to the local council to rent an apartment and had been told that as a single woman she faced a long wait. But soon afterward she'd been offered a small place in a block that everyone else shied away from because of the persistent vandalism of the local unemployed lads. In desperation she took it. That was her darkest moment.

The turning point had come when Joan, another secretary at Kinroy & Son had found her reading the financial pages of the newspaper while she had her morning coffee. She'd always done this when Andrew was alive, and he'd explained everything to her, delighting in her sharp brain that could hold a stream of complicated figures—just like his own.

Since his death she'd repeatedly told herself that she should abandon the habit, but somehow it clung. She found that she knew many of the people she read about and, because of Andrew's addiction to scurrilous gossip, was aware of certain facts about them that seemed to be hidden from the financial writers.

"Swank," Joan had jeered amiably. "You don't really understand that stuff, do you?"

"Yes," Rae had said, surprised.

"What are all those figures and funny words?"

"What funny words?"

"Well—" Joan peered over her shoulder to read, " 'Equity stake, third tier market.' What on earth are they?"

Rae told her and realized that Joan was staring.

"Heavens, you must be some kind of genius. What are you doing here?"

It was as though someone had thrown open a window. It hadn't occurred to Rae that her easy grasp of finance set her apart, but for the first time she saw a way of escape.

She began inquiries about the financial careers that might be open to her, and received excellent advice from her father's one-time secretary, a neat, efficient woman who was now working for a firm of stock brokers.

"You must get some qualifications," Mrs. Carter had said. "A degree in economics would be your best bet."

"But I'd never get into university. Andrew took me out of school before I passed any exams. He said they didn't matter for me," Rae had said in despair.

"Then enroll in the Open University. You don't need exam passes for that. It's for people who can't study full-time. You do your normal job by day and study in the evenings and weekends. It's a slow process, but it's recognized everywhere as the equal of a conventional degree."

That very day Rae found the necessary address, and wrote off. A week later she was enrolled in the economics course at the Open University. From that moment on her life was altered. Her job was still boring, but she had rediscovered hope.

Rae was on the last lap of her studies. She'd passed all the preliminary exams well, but in the final year the work was harder. Still her hope persisted. There were just six more months to get through.

Seated at her tiny dressing table, she started work on her face as unsentimentally as an actress making up for a performance, which was how she thought of these evenings. Champagne dinner and dancing at a luxury hotel meant full war paint.

After thirty minutes she was transformed to her own satisfaction. On her head she wore the red wig that she kept for these occasions because it helped her draw a clear line between her real self and her "self for hire" as she called it. Together with the gold dress, the wig gave her an exotic, lioness quality totally at variance with her natural, understated beauty.

The makeup was as unsubtle as everything else. The generous curves of her lips were accentuated, the eyes darkened and seemingly enlarged.

The true message in her expressive face was one that the men who hired her for the evening never noticed. It could be found in the chin that for all its daintiness had a stubborn set, and the lovely eyes that could darken into hatred at the mention of one name. That name was Giles Blake, the man who had crucified her father and herself and in doing so had laid the foundations for a phenomenally successful career for himself.

Sometimes, during those eight years, she'd glanced at trial reports in the newspaper and found that the name Giles Blake cropped up with increasing frequency. Very occasionally he would appear for the defense, but most often he was the prosecuting attorney. He was at his best, she thought bitterly, when on the attack.

A year earlier there'd been a press outcry about high lawyers' fees. In a froth of indignation, one of the popular dailies had printed an estimate of what several of the top ones were likely to earn. Giles Blake's name had been on that list and the amount quoted had made Rae's eyebrows shoot up. He'd become a very successful man on the foundation of her father's destruction.

The old dream of revenge had never died. If she'd had the slightest hope that her client tonight might be the same man, her eyes would have sparkled with joy at the thought of encountering him again and perhaps striking a blow for her father's memory. But it could be no more than coincidence that this man bore the same name. Handsome and assured, successful and wealthy, Giles Blake would never need to hire a woman.

When she was ready, she called the local minicab service. Her home was "out of bounds," and she never allowed a man to collect her there or bring her back afterward.

Giles Blake lived in a wealthy suburb on the far side of London. It was an area Rae knew well. As Tanis Haines, she'd had friends who lived there, but since the trial she hadn't been back to see them. Now she had the eerie sensation that her old life was unfolding before her as the car drove through attractive, tree-lined streets and finally stopped in front of wrought-iron gates. Through them she could see a red brick mansion, set well back from the road. Parked just in front of it was a gleaming silver Rolls-Royce.

Rae walked up the drive, thankful that the rain had stopped. At the heavy oak door, she rang the bell and waited. After a moment the door was opened by a middle-aged woman.

"I'm Rae Bonham," she said. "I'm expected."

"Oh, yes. Come in, will you. I'll tell Mr. Blake you're here."

The maid showed Rae into a room that overlooked the drive and left her. Rae discarded the mink jacket, for the heating was on and she was uncomfortably warm. There was a huge mirror over the mantelpiece, and she used it to make a last-minute check on her appearance. The gold dress was admirable. It had been cleverly designed to seem more daring than it actually was. The two dainty straps that held it up left her shoulders almost completely bare, giving the effect of décolletage. In fact, only the swell of her full breasts was revealed before the material modestly enclosed them.

Rae combed a few stray curls into place and then began to look around her, trying to deduce her client's character from his surroundings. The room was quietly elegant in a traditional style. The colors were all muted, with a predominance of beige, brown and yellow. The large sofa was overstuffed and upholstered in wild silk. Rae had been raised in luxurious surroundings, and at once her knowing eye recognized the quality of everything in the room. The chairs, she was sure, were genuine Chippendale, and the walls were hung with fine prints that looked as if they'd been chosen without regard to cost.

She had a disturbing sensation of something wrong. A young, wealthy man could attract beautiful female company without having to hire it by the evening. Sally had said Giles Blake was young, and her eyes told her that he was extremely wealthy.

Rae began to search the room more closely, looking for clues to the mystery. Gradually she realized that there was a surprising lack of ornaments. The only decorative touch to break the severity was a large photograph of two children that dominated a delicate eighteenth-century desk. Rae moved closer.

The picture showed a girl and boy, both dark-haired and probably under ten. They had bright, mischievous faces, so alike that they were obviously brother and sister. As Rae studied the picture a faint anticipatory excitement began to run along her nerves, for she recognized the face those children shared. She'd seen it once before, staring at her across a courtroom. It was the face of the man she'd hate till the day she died.

"Miss Bonham?"

Rae whirled and saw Giles Blake.

He'd come silently into the room and was standing watching her. She gazed back at him, her heart thumping with bitter joy.

He was in his mid-thirties and perhaps a little more solid than he'd been at twenty-eight. But Rae saw only his face, and everything in it was just as she remembered: the dark, deep-set eyes below the high forehead, the chin that was firm to the point of obstinacy, the unexpected curve of the mouth, as though nature had tried to add a touch of generosity to the coldly perfect features.

His mouth drew her gaze. She'd fixed her attention on it once before when it had poured out clever, cruel words that damned her and her father. Now she realized that there was a change in him, after all. The hint of arrogance about the lips, once a mere shadow, had become marked with the passage of years.

The look he gave her was frankly appraising. He was sizing her up, estimating whether what he'd bought was worth the price he'd paid. For a moment Rae was assailed by a qualm. It surely wasn't possible that he'd recognized her? She'd changed more than he had, and the wig altered her dramatically. She took a deep breath. There was only one thing to do with danger and that was to meet it head-on.

She began to walk toward him, moving with a slow, sensuous grace, allowing her hips to swivel a little, knowing that the dress clung lovingly to her contours. He stayed where he was, watching her advance, taking in every fluid movement, and a gleam of satisfaction came into his eyes.

"Yes," she said when she'd stopped before him. "I'm Rae Bonham. You must be Mr. Blake, my employer."

She'd modulated her voice down a couple of notes, and as she spoke she gave her head a little shake so that the red curls danced about her face. The effect was just as she'd hoped. His eyes never left her. They lingered on her wide, deceptively candid eyes, the deliberately seductive curve of her mouth, the pearly whiteness of her bare shoulders and the swell of her breasts. She had the feeling that he was absorbing everything about her all at once, not with his eyes or his mind, but through every pore of his being, as though her body lay against his.

She tried to thrust the thought away, but it wouldn't be dismissed. Her physical awareness of him was equally intense. He was taller than she'd thought. In the witness box she'd been looking down on him and hadn't realized that he was over six feet. But now his broad-shouldered, muscular frame towered several inches above her.

He didn't look like a man who worked indoors at a sedentary job. He hadn't an ounce of spare flesh. His figure was athletic and his face deeply tanned. he wore a black dinner jacket, black bow tie and snowy white embroidered evening shirt against which the brown of his skin stood out in stark contrast.

Rae took all this in, but something else about him struck her far more forcibly—an air of tension that was like an aura round him. Giles Blake lived on his nerves, and those nerves were strung to breaking point. This was a man who kept himself under a control so stern that it amounted to repression. The effort filled him with strain, perhaps because he suspected that it wasn't entirely successful. Rae had the impression of banked fires smoldering and ready to break out unexpectedly.

After a long moment, he seemed to wrench himself out of a hypnotic trance.

"Your employer?" he echoed.

"Well, you're paying my wages this evening, aren't you?" she said, still in the same deep voice.

"Yes, I suppose you could say I am."

"I do hope you feel you're getting full value for money, Mr. Blake." As she said this Rae gave the confident laugh of a beautiful woman who knows she need fear no man's judgment.

But instead of giving the routine compliment that her question should have provoked, Giles Blake said simply, "I always get full value for money, Miss Bonham. I insist on it." He indicated the drinks cabinet by the window. "We have time for a drink before we go. What will you have?"

"Dry sherry, please."

"How much did the agency tell you?" he said as he handed her a glass and seated himself opposite her.

"Very little—only the name of the hotel, that there'd be dinner and dancing and I was to dress up to the occasion." She put her head on one side provocatively. "Will I do you credit?"

His eyes flickered over her, taking in the pearly sheen of her shoulders, the contours of her high breasts.

"I should think you'll cause a sensation," he said in a dryly ironic tone. "That's what I'm hiring you for."

"Why don't you tell me exactly why you *are* hiring me? I can't play the part properly if I don't have the script. Why is it important that I should make a sensation?"

"Because," he said harshly, "my divorce became final today, and I'm damned if I'm going to have them thinking I care."

So that was it. Now she understood the bare room and the children's photograph.

"Who's 'them'?" she said. "The people we'll meet tonight?"

"Partly, although it's more than that. I'm a lawyer. Belinda, my ex-wife, is the daughter of a judge. The dinner we're going to tonight has been arranged by a legal charity. The people there will be my colleagues and their wives, virtually every one of whom knows Belinda and knows that she left me. Some of them will even know that the divorce came through today. Do you imagine they won't be watching me?"

Rae thought it very probable that every eye would be on him, eagerly seeking some sign of discomfiture. The arrogance so clearly marked in his face and manner must have won him many enemies, apart from herself.

"Why did your wife leave you?" she asked.

His mouth tightened in anger. "There's not the slightest need for you to know that."

"Of course there is," she said. "Doubtless everyone else there will know. It'll look rather odd if I'm the only one in ignorance. People will start to wonder. If you want them to think I'm a real girlfriend, you should tell me whatever you'd tell me if I was."

He scowled, but the logic of this got through to him.

"Very well," he said. "Belinda left me for another man. Their wedding is planned for next week. She also happens to be carrying his child."

He spoke the words as though he had to drag every one of them out by force and Rae could easily guess at the savage blow his wife had dealt his pride. She tried to look sympathetic and conceal the fact that inwardly she was rejoicing.

"Those two children in the photograph . . . ?" she said.

"They're Belinda's and mine. Their names are Melanie and James. She took them with her," said Giles flatly in a tone that didn't invite further questions.

"Have you decided on our cover story?" she asked between sips of sherry.

"Our what?"

"What do I say if someone asks me how we met?"

"I can't say I'd thought of it," he said.

"Unless you want people to suspect the truth, we have to concoct something. Could your mother have introduced us?"

"My mother is dead and —" he looked her over wryly "—she isn't likely to have been acquainted with you."

"You mean she'd have thought I was a hussy?" said Rae daringly.

Unexpectedly he grinned. For a moment his eyes held nothing but amusement, briefly banishing the coldness from his face and transforming him in a way that disturbed her.

"You *are* a hussy," he said. "I knew that when I saw your picture in the agency. That's why I chose you and not one of the others. They didn't have what you have."

"What *exactly* do I have, Mr. Blake?" she purred provocatively.

"You don't need me to put it into words," he said coolly. "A woman who flaunts it as you do plainly knows she has it."

She gave him her most wide-eyed, childlike stare, and her voice hovered on the edge of a chuckle.

"Oh, but I'd so like to know what name you'd put to it," she said demurely.

It was on the tip of his tongue to say bluntly that she was a sexy little piece, but the words wouldn't form themselves, and what came out was quite different.

"God help the man who's fool enough to fall in love with you," he said abruptly. "You could give him heaven or hell."

Then, to his intense annoyance, he felt himself reddening. She wondered what had come over him to say such a thing. To complete his embarrassment he noticed that this disturbing young woman had lost none of her composure. She sat there in her glossy wrappings, looking strangely like a child who'd just received an unexpected gift, but there was an undercurrent of amusement in her manner that discomfited him even more.

"And do you think you're in any danger of falling in love with me, Mr. Blake?" she asked, smiling.

"None whatever," he said sharply.

"Not even for the sake of heaven or hell?"

"Is this your usual manner of talking to clients?" he demanded, his eyes narrowing.

It was far from her usual manner. Rae's evenings out always ended with a chaste good-night, and out of fairness to the man she made this plain from the start. But tonight was a special occasion. Fate had delivered her enemy into her hands, and to keep him there she must play the wanton. So she threw herself into the role while her mind coolly planned the coming evening, an evening she intended Giles Blake to remember as long as he lived.

"That . . . depends on the client," she said softly, looking at him from beneath her lashes.

With a swiftness that took her by surprise he rose, grasping her wrist and pulling her to her feet in one abrupt movement. Before she'd devined his intention, his arms were around her, pulling her fiercely against him. As he dropped his head, Rae had one brief glimpse of his eyes. They were full of rage.

His lips were hard on hers. It wasn't a kiss so much as a declaration of intent. He took possession of her mouth as though by right, and at first her soul rose in outrage against him. Her hands flew upward to push him away and her body writhed in his grasp. But at the last minute she remembered her revenge and fought down her hostility. Instead of jerking away from him, she forced her hands to caress his shoulders. At once he deepened the kiss, easing his tongue into her mouth in one expert movement. It flickered against the soft inner flesh, exploring, challenging. Then suddenly it was gone and her mouth was free—free, that is, except for the burning imprint of his that lingered on it like a brand.

She was breathless with the suddenness of what had happened to her, and her heart was beating wildly. In his arms she'd known a shattering sensation. It was something for which she couldn't find a name, but she knew she'd had it once before.

Then the answer came to her. In the court on that day long ago, when she'd first set eyes on Giles Blake, she'd had the same feeling then. It was the sensation that would make the fur stand up on an animal's back, an awareness of overwhelming danger.

Then the danger had filled her with fear. But tonight she held the upper hand, and she felt only excitement. She knew it must have brought color to her cheeks and a sparkle to her eyes, and that Giles was watching her closely. She flung her head back and laughed recklessly in his face. His eyes gleamed in appreciation.

"At least we understand each other, Miss Bonham," he said huskily. "Unfortunately we have to go to this function tonight or they'll say I'm afraid to show my face. Otherwise—"

She drew away from him and assumed a demure expression.

"I'm sure the agency explained to you that the terms include only my company *in public* for one evening, Mr. Blake."

"Yes, they did, and to hell with the agency. Whatever's between us, we'll make the terms ourselves."

"Do you think there's going to be anything between us?" she challenged him.

"You know there has to be," he said, watching her face intently.

"Perhaps," she said with a careless shrug.

"There's no perhaps about it. What game are you playing? You led me on. Don't deny it."

"I don't. It's just—well, it's getting late, and surely there'll be a more convenient moment to discuss all this . . . later."

"Yes," he said, drawing a ragged breath. "You're right, Miss Bonham. We must be going." He was angry with himself for an uncharacteristic loss of control.

She gave a little laugh. "Surely we're long past the point where you could call me Rae?"

With difficulty he managed to laugh in return. "Yes, and my name is Giles."

He placed her jacket round her shoulders. It seemed to her that he allowed his fingers to linger against her skin, and again the excitement forked through her like lightning. She hadn't known that danger could be so electrifying.

He drove the Rolls-Royce himself, handling it in heavy traffic with the confidence of a man who wasn't afraid of costly things. Rae turned slightly in her seat so she could watch him, noting the way his strong, shapely hands lay against the steering wheel, and how the passing lights briefly illuminated his harshly attractive features. He was a handsome man, and he had the charisma that comes with authority and success. Under any other circumstances, she'd have felt her peace of mind threatened.

"There's one thing about you that puzzles me," she said at last.

"What's that?"

"Why did you have to hire a girlfriend for tonight? An attractive man like you surely isn't short of female friends."

"Most of my female friends are the wives of my colleagues. As for the ones who are unmarried, there'd be practical problems. A woman who knew me would see through the device, unless I pretended to feelings I don't have, which would disgust me and be unfair to her."

"You could always tell her the truth, as you've done with me."

"And have her gossip about me to our mutual friends afterward? No, thank you."

His shudder was almost imperceptible, but she sensed it in her bones.

"You'd really hate that, wouldn't you?" she mused. "Being talked about—"

"And being laughed at. I won't tolerate being made to look a fool," he said firmly.

There was no further discussion between them, but as they drove on, Rae was smiling in the darkness at the simplicity of this clever man.

Two

We still haven't decided on our cover story,'' said Rae as they neared the hotel. ''Could we have met on holiday?''

''I never take holidays,'' he said. ''Not the lounging on the beach kind, anyway. I've tried, but by the second day I'm bored and thinking of all the things I could be doing.''

''How familiar that sounds,'' she said abstractedly.

''Why? Do you know someone else like that? If so, I pity you. I've been reliably informed that we're impossible to live with.''

She thought of Andrew, also a workaholic, and realized how incautious she'd been to let the remark slip out.

''What about your tan?'' she said, steering the conversation into safer waters. ''You didn't get that in wet and windy England.''

''I've spent part of the summer in Rome.''

''That's more encouraging.''

''Researching a book comparing Continental with English law.'' He took a sideways glance at her face and grinned. ''I'm not very helpful, am I?''

"It doesn't matter. I've been to Rome. I can keep my end up in a conversation."

She'd visited Rome in the last summer before the trial and still had vivid memories of it. They managed to identify those parts of the city they both knew, and decide that they'd met in a small restaurant near St. Peter's, where he'd tripped over her feet. Rae invented the script of this meeting almost single-handed. Giles's mind was most at home with solid facts. Fantasy was very hard for him.

"Why did you leave it till the last minute to book me?" she said suddenly. "You must have had the date fixed long ago."

"I had no intention of coming, at all. Then I realized that Belinda had automatically booked us two places months ago, as she did every year. I suddenly saw those two empty chairs and people sniggering."

"But you didn't come into the agency until lunchtime. Didn't you remember till this morning?"

"You want to know a great deal, don't you?" he said, scowling. "No, of course I remembered before today. My secretary reminded me a week ago. It's just that—" He shrugged.

It's just that it took you till today to sink your pride, she thought, remembering Sally's words, "...never been to an agency before, and didn't like finding himself in one..."

A few minutes later, they reached the hotel. It was an old establishment that combined discreet luxury with prestige. They were among the last to arrive. As they stood in the corridor waiting to enter the huge dining room, Rae could look through the open double doors and see the other guests. Like Giles, the men were all dressed in black dinner jackets, white evening shirts and black bow ties. Few of them, she guessed, were under fifty. Only the most successful, and therefore probably the older, lawyers could afford this expensive function.

The women were sedate matrons, dressed in pastel shades. Some were younger than their husbands, a few were probably daughters, many were attractive. But none of them had Rae's vivid, glowing loveliness, or that indefinable extra allure that is more than beauty, and that she had in abundance. In that muted gathering, she knew, without conceit, that she would be like a bird of paradise landed among wrens. Looking up, she caught Giles's smoldering eyes on her and knew he was thinking the same.

The proceedings were formal. After a moment, they stepped forward, Giles gave their names to a steward who trumpeted into the room, *"Mr. Giles Blake and Miss Rae Bonham."*

At first only a few people near the door turned to look at them. But something about their stillness caught the attention of their neighbors, who also fell silent and grew still. Necks were craned, eyes opened a little wider. Rae looked neither to the right nor to the left as she advanced into the room, her hand tucked demurely in Giles's arm. She seemed oblivious to the male jaws that dropped, the female eyes that narrowed at the sight of her.

A man came forward. He was in his mid-forties, with pleasant, unremarkable features and thinning ginger hair.

"Hello, Giles. Nice to see you here," he said breezily. "Thought perhaps you weren't coming."

"Why on earth shouldn't I, Harris?" said Giles, and his rich bass contained only amusement.

"Ah—" Harris gave a short, embarrassed laugh. "Blowed if I know." But though he spoke to Giles, his eyes were on Rae.

"Darling—" Giles leaned down a little toward her "—this sinister character angling for an introduction is Harris Bland, a colleague of mine, and one of the organizers of this event. Harris, meet Rae Bonham."

"Your table's this way," he said. "It's the same as mine."

The seating was arranged at dozens of small round tables. As they made their way to theirs, Rae had a confused impression of her surroundings. She was in a large room, decorated by banks of flowers and lit by chandeliers. Long gilt mirrors were built into the walls, and near the table a space cleared suddenly, giving her a full-length view of herself and Giles.

They were a golden couple, she realized. Her own luminous beauty was offset by his height and dark, handsome grace. Giles was almost the youngest man there, and into Rae's mind came the rumors that had reached her at Andrew's trial, "Years ahead of his contemporaries...the best man of his generation...trouble is, he knows it...consumed by ambition...."

She and Andrew had been the victims of Giles's ambition. She must never let herself forget that. She turned cold as she recalled how close she'd come to doing so. As the two reflections advanced across the floor together, the woman so radiant in her beauty, the man so splendid in his proud assurance, the treacherous thought had crossed her mind that they looked as though they'd been made to be together.

Each place at the table was marked by a card bearing a name. As Harris ushered Rae to her seat he turned red suddenly and snatched up the card, but not before she had time to see the name Mrs. Belinda Blake.

"The cards were made out from the steward's list," he explained hastily. "I suppose they didn't know."

"While you're changing cards, Harris, you can change mine," came an elderly but robust voice.

An old man had risen and was determinedly shouldering everyone out of his way. Before anyone could stop him—if anyone had dared—he'd picked up Giles's card and dropped it by his own plate. Then he firmly laid his own at the place next to Rae. She glanced uncertainly across at the old lady next to the now empty place. She was a small birdlike creature with twinkling eyes and an unexpectedly powerful voice.

"It's all right, my dear, I'm his sister," she boomed with a rich chuckle. "The old fool always does this. Privilege of age."

"Privilege of age, nothing," growled the old man. "Privilege of rank! What's the point of being a judge if you can't use it to collar the loveliest woman in the room?"

It was impossible to be offended by him. Rae smiled as Giles introduced him as Judge Lorrimer and felt her hand engulfed in a gnarled fist.

"Giles, you're a dark dog," said the old judge. "Where have you been hiding her? Never mind—it'll be more fun to find out for myself."

He pulled Rae's chair out for her with a gallant flourish. Giles seated himself beside the judge's sister. Rae glanced across to see how he was taking this development and saw that he was pleased with the stir she'd created. Men were casting him frankly envious glances, and Judge Lorrimer shamelessly intended to monopolize her.

She was at ease in this gathering. During Andrew's life, his house had overflowed with his guests, entirely drawn from the business world. From an early age, Rae had been used to the company of men whose understated appearance belied their power. Lawyers, she discovered, had much in common with financiers.

The judge, who might have been about seventy, flirted with her with an old-world courtesy that didn't conceal his relish, and every man at the table seemed to have something to say to her. The women, when they'd finished examining Rae, turned their attention to Giles, studying him, Rae guessed, for the telltale signs that would reveal his feelings about her, but he was too well mannered to neglect the judge's elderly sister.

The dinner drew to a conclusion. Coffee and liqueurs were served. At the head table, a man rose and adjusted a microphone. Conversation died as people gave him their polite attention. He introduced another man to talk about the charity everyone was there to support. There was a vote of thanks, speeches, more speeches.

Rae heard none of it. She was acutely conscious of Giles's eyes fixed on her, full of a heated, disturbing light. Free of the obligation to make small talk, he could let his gaze follow his thoughts. Rae wondered about those thoughts. His desire for her was unmistakable, but it was tinged with something else, something that she couldn't read. But it brought a frown to his dark eyes.

She returned his look, allowing a little smile to play on her lips. She saw the sudden movement of his shoulders as he drew in his breath sharply. The severity of his features softened, and the hard line of his mouth relaxed into a curve that hinted at a sensuality lurking not far below the surface.

The imprint of his lips seemed to be on hers still, haunting her with the awareness of barely controlled fires that she'd sensed in that blazing moment when he'd held her against him. She tried to brush the thought aside, but instead found herself wondering how he'd be if he yielded to those fires. Would the lover be as stern and contained as the man? What would it be like to challenge him to the point of explosion, piercing the veneer of control that he wore like armor?

Then she chided herself. Behind that veneer lay nothing but hard emptiness. Giles Blake cared only for his career and the respect of his peers. Those were the chinks in his armor by which she would humble him as he'd humbled her.

The speeches were over. Some of the tables were being moved to the side of the room, clearing a space for dancing. A small band was taking its position, the chandeliers were extinguished, and waiters went round lighting the candles on the tables.

People were leaving their places, moving from table to table. Judge Lorrimer hailed an old friend and departed, leaving an empty chair that Giles quickly filled.

"Watch!" he said, grinning. "Suddenly every man in this room is going to remember something he's been meaning to say to me."

He was right. The next half hour was lost in a whirl of introductions. Rae was good at remembering names and faces, but even she eventually became lost. At the end, only one man stood out. His name was Alec Craxton, and she noticed him specially because of Giles's obvious dislike for the man.

"He's an idiot," he said when she queried this.

Rae would have called Alec a professional charmer, a little too smooth and easy to be genuinely charming, but pleasant enough company for an evening.

"What really lies behind it, of course, is Belinda," murmured Harris into Rae's ear during a quiet moment.

Giles was briefly occupied elsewhere, and Rae murmured, "You mean that's the man she . . . ?"

"Oh, no, no! The man she's going to marry is an academic. But Alec was her first fling. Nothing in it, really. I think she was just trying to get Giles's attention away from his work for five minutes. Nobody takes Alec seriously. But it all got rather out of hand. I think the marriage was pretty dead after that, and it was only a matter of time before Belinda found her professor."

So Alec Craxton had inflicted a public failure on Giles, and Giles resented him accordingly. Rae studied Alec, who was tall, fair and elegant. He was relaxed and easy, as though he felt at home wherever he happened to be, and this contrasted sharply with Giles's air of tension that never quite left him, even when he was laughing.

The band struck up the first dance. Harris looked at Rae.

"I wonder if—" he began.

"No, certainly not," Giles cut in on him amiably. He reached out a hand and drew Rae to her feet. In another moment they were on the dance floor and he'd taken her into his arms for a waltz.

"If dinner had lasted much longer, I'd have wrung Judge Lorrimer's neck," he said.

"Am I doing well?" she murmured.

"You know how well you're doing. There isn't a man in the place who can take his eyes off you, or a woman who wouldn't like to murder you."

"The evening's a success for you, then?"

He looked down at her, his mouth disturbingly close.

"Don't worry," he said with a hint of irony. "You'll get your reward."

"I'm not worried about my reward, Mr. Blake," she said in a consciously prim voice. "The fee you paid to the agency in advance will be passed on to me, minus the agency commission, of course."

He laughed. "That's not the reward I was talking about, and you know it. I can't promise to compete with the man who gave you that mink jacket but—"

"Don't try," she said abruptly. "You couldn't compete with him in a million years."

He drew back an inch. "Did I touch a raw nerve? Who was he? What happened?"

"Nothing that would interest you," she said, smiling again.

She was glad he'd reminded her of Andrew and brought her mind back to this evening's true purpose. For a moment, as he held her closely against the length of his hard body, she'd almost forgotten it. The sensation of danger was with her again.

Rae's first love had been a hero-worshiping infatuation for an older man, a banking colleague of her father's. Andrew had been pleased, and if things had gone otherwise they might have been married by now. But when the world exploded in her face, her hero had unheroically distanced himself.

When she was twenty-two, Derek had appeared in her life. He'd come from nowhere, professed himself bowled over by her, then swept her off her feet and into his bed. It had been her first experience in physical passion, and if it had been less than ecstatic she'd put that down to her own awkwardness. She was overwhelmed by Derek, by his kindness and tenderness but most of all by his love for her. The bitter time since the trial had dissolved in the magic of finding someone who loved and wanted her.

Then the bomb had exploded.

Quite casually Derek had let fall that he'd known who she was from the start. Wasn't it, he'd suggested, time she dropped the poverty-stricken act, and let on where she'd hidden Andrew's money?

It had taken her a month to convince him that she hadn't managed to salvage any of her father's fortune, and after that she'd never seen Derek again.

Since then, she'd had a number of casual boyfriends, but she'd drawn back from deeper involvement, and the ease with which she'd managed this had convinced her that she was a cold woman, both emotionally and physically.

Now, unexpectedly, she was experiencing sensations that she'd thought were over for her. Giles's hand on the small of her back held her insistently against him, so she could feel the warmth of his body through her clothes. She was alarmingly aware how thin was the material that covered her. But more alarming still was the desire she could sense in him, communicating itself to her through the hand that held hers, calling forth her unwilling response.

She had the impression that everything in the world had slowed down. Her limbs felt heavy with unaccustomed warmth, and she was drifting in a dream. Yet, dreamlike also, she seemed to stand apart and watch a man and woman in each other's arms, lost to everything but their awareness of each other.

She wanted to call to the woman and warn her that she'd set her feet on a perilous road, one whose end she couldn't see. Strangest of all, she wanted to call to the man and warn him that he stood on the edge of an abyss, for she could see that his face held a naked, unguarded look, as though he'd been surprised by some emotion beyond his power to deal with. He was vulnerable with the terrifying vulnerability of the very strong who have never had to learn their own weakness. He held the woman with an intensity that seemed to absorb his whole being, leaving him unprotected, because he didn't know that she hated him.

Rae's heart was behaving in an unusual and unsettling manner. Its slow, pounding rhythm seemed to be invading her whole body, so that even her fingertips pulsed gently against his hand, and the hot breath that caressed her shoulder told her that his breathing had deepened. She had a sudden feeling of being naked in his arms, as though he'd willed it so by the power of thought.

"What's the matter?" he said. "You stiffened suddenly."

"Nothing! It's just that the dance is coming to an end. I'd like to sit down."

He frowned at the sudden sharpness in her voice, but led her back to their table. Judge Lorrimer had returned, and his eyes lit up at the sight of her. Rae took a deep breath. Then she slid into the seat beside him and gave a noisy hiccup, followed by a giggle.

"Ooh, dear," she said, apparently overcome by confusion. "Listen to me!"

"Would you like some coffee?" said the judge gallantly.

She eyed him mournfully. "It's a bit late for that," she intoned with a slow, careful emphasis of someone watching every word. For good measure, she ended with another dramatic hiccup.

There were some puzzled frowns around the table. Glances were exchanged. Rae looked up to find Giles scowling at her. She beamed at him innocently.

"Sorry, darling," she said, her voice very slightly slurred. "I know I promised, but you know how it is." She giggled. "I guess I just shouldn't promise."

Giles moved toward her, but he wasn't quick enough. Alec Craxton, who'd been watching the developments with the eyes of a cat, slipped in beside her.

"Good resolutions are absolutely fatal," he agreed. "I gave up making them long ago. It saved so many apologies."

"Why, you're *right*," she sang with tipsy merriment. "Think of the apologies I'm going to have to make after tonight."

"A beautiful woman should never apologize," he told her.

"Oh, aren't you *nice*!" She draped an arm around his neck and spoke confidingly. "Do you know, I've been looking at you all evening and thinking when is that *attractive* man going to ask me to dance?"

"To hear is to obey," he said with a flourish and rose, taking her hand. For a moment it looked as though Giles might intervene by force, but he held back as though reluctant to make a scene. His face was dark with fury.

Alec swept her onto the floor. The music had grown much livelier, and the two of them flung themselves into an energetic dance. Rae was an expert dancer, and luckily so was Alec. Their technical bravura drew attention, and a space was cleared to let them perform. Few people had noticed that anything was wrong.

Out of the corner of her eye, Rae was aware of a crowd watching them. In the blur she couldn't make out details, but she knew, as surely as if she could see him, that Giles was watching her with eyes black with rage. He'd miss nothing, including the slinky, sinuous movements of her hips and her shapely flashing legs when the swirl of the dress revealed them. Most of all, he'd see her head flung back, her lips parted in ecstasy, her seeming absorption in her partner.

The music ended with a crash. On the last note, Alec seized her in a dramatic embrace. At once she wrapped her arms around his neck and sagged against him, apparently on the verge of passing out. He assisted her to the table, and she threw herself into a seat with exaggerated relief.

Suddenly Alec had disappeared. Giles was there, taking hold of her firmly.

"We're leaving now," he grated.

"Oh, no, darling," she cooed. "Not *yet*! Not till I've had just one more little drink."

She went off into a fit of laughter, throwing her head back and looking at Giles under her lashes. The sight that met her eyes eased the pain of eight years. Giles was learning what it was like to be destroyed in public—just as she had been.

"Rae—" His hand was on her arm.

"I don't want to go with you," she said with a clever assumption of tipsy petulance. "Why should I? I don't know you—never saw you before today. Wouldn't people laugh if they knew about *that*? Oh, I could tell a thing or two—"

She got no further. Giles's hand had tightened, hauling her to her feet. For a moment his eyes blazed into hers and she knew, with a stab of alarm, that he was losing his control. Then her surroundings were flying past her as Giles hurried her from the room so fast that her feet barely touched the floor.

The crowd parted in front of them. The double doors opened. Giles swept her irresistibly onward, looking neither right nor left. She began to wonder how far he intended to haul her.

Halfway down the corridor, he stopped in front of a door, flung it open and dragged her through. They were in a small cloakroom, but Rae had no chance to notice more because Giles slammed the door behind him and stood facing her with anger in his eyes. He'd released her arm. She knew she'd have bruises the next day where his fingers had been, but she didn't care. Her blood was pounding with exhilaration. She'd struck a blow for Andrew.

"You two-faced scheming little bitch," he said murderously. "You're not drunk. You did that on purpose. Why? Who put you up to it? My God, I knew I had enemies, but no one who'd stoop to this. You're not getting out of this room until you tell me who it was. Now *talk*!''

''Nobody put me up to it,'' she said defiantly.

He took a step toward her. ''Don't play games with me,'' he said in a soft, deadly voice. ''You have three seconds to tell me who's behind this. One—''

''All right, I'll tell you,'' she flung at him. ''Andrew Haines, that's who's behind this.''

''What the devil are you talking about?'' he demanded. ''Andrew Haines is dead.''

''Yes. Andrew Haines is dead, *but his daughter isn't.*''

She stepped back from him and reached up a hand to the red wig. With a swift movement she pulled it off, and her mass of fair hair came tumbling about her face.

For a long moment Giles stared at her, his face the color of parchment. He looked as though he'd received a blow in the stomach.

''You?'' he said at last in a disbelieving voice. *''You!''*

''I told you I'd come back,'' she said.

Three

You," Giles echoed again blankly as though the one word was all he could utter.

"Yes, me," she said. "Tanis Haines. I wasn't hired by your enemies. I *am* your enemy."

He was so silent that she knew an eerie feeling. His face was white, except for the dark eyes that scorched her with their light.

"I thought there was something familiar about your face," he said at last, slowly. "When I saw your picture in the agency, and then tonight—I *knew* there was something—but I couldn't place it."

"I didn't intend you to. It wouldn't have suited me for you to recognize me too soon."

"Before you had the chance to humiliate me in front of almost everyone I know," he said, his voice becoming vibrant again as anger returned.

"That's right. I hope it'll be a long time before you dare show your face to them again—just as I had to hide my face after what you did to my father and me."

"You vindictive little brat," he breathed furiously. "Are you cherishing the illusion that he was innocent? Andrew Haines was the biggest crook in creation. I didn't conduct a personal campaign against him. I did my job—a job someone would have had to do."

"But not everyone would have done it the way you did," she said, her face as white as his.

"What do you mean by that?"

"You know what I mean. You didn't just prosecute my father. You went for the jugular because you had a career to make and a lot of important people were watching you. It was a big case for you, wasn't it? So you made the most of it. It didn't matter who got destroyed in the process, as long as Giles Blake came out looking good."

"You're wrong, Miss Haines," he said, his eyes snapping. "I did care for the people who were destroyed. I cared for all the small defenseless people who were ruined because they depended on firms your father bankrupted, often deliberately because that meant a bigger profit for him. Why can't you face the truth about him? He was as guilty as hell and he got what was coming to him."

"Did you have to crucify him?" she cried. "Did you have to twist my words so that he thought I was betraying him?"

"I never twisted your words—"

"You did," she said, choking with remembered grief. "You seized on little points and hammered away at them so everything was distorted. You made me say things I never meant to say—"

"I cross-examined you, which was my job. I was there to establish your father's guilt. How did you think I was going to do that? By having a friendly chat? What you interpret as 'twisting' was nothing but a normal cross-examination."

"You mean," she said, looking at him curiously, "that what you did to me was normal procedure?"

"Perfectly normal," he replied shortly.

"Perhaps it is," she said slowly. "I don't know. I'm not a lawyer. But when I consider a world in which such distortion of the truth is normal procedure, I can only say that I am glad I am not.''

In the dead silence that followed, he drew in his breath painfully. He, the skilled courtroom orator, so expert at leading other men into traps of their own making, had walked into this one like a child. This woman, standing here looking at him with hate in her mysteriously innocent eyes, had prepared it for him. But he knew he'd laid the foundations himself, eight years ago.

''What's the matter?'' she taunted him. ''Don't you recognize your own words, Mr. Blake?''

''Yes,'' he said with difficulty. ''I recognize them.''

He could hardly bear to look at her. He was filled with confusion that robbed him of speech. His golden tongue was his defense against the world. Without it he felt naked.

He wondered what she'd say if he told her that she'd lived in his mind all these years, not as a continuous presence, but as a pale ghost who returned to torment him whenever he was least prepared. She'd ruined his great moment by forcing him to see himself in a light that shocked him. The words ''you smug, self-satisfied bastard!'' had stayed with him, poisoning what should have been the enjoyable memory of his first major victory.

A thousand times he'd dismissed her outburst as the inevitable reaction of someone who'd come off worst from a brush with the law. It was easy to explain it all away in the comfortable formal phrases that he was at home with. But the little ghost had always returned, refusing to be silenced so easily.

Her desperate face, tear stained and distorted with grief, as he'd last seen it, had haunted him when other cases and other witnesses had faded to nothing. Now he forced himself to turn and look at it in the flesh, amazed that he hadn't recognized it tonight, despite the red wig.

But it had changed, he realized. It was the same face but older, marked by experience and tragic knowledge. In place of the bland innocence of eighteen was reckless defiance. The occasional stabs of guilt he'd felt over that sad girl were, he now knew, a waste of time. She'd turned into a woman capable of using her astonishing beauty to avenge herself. At the thought of how he'd foolishly succumbed to that beauty, bitterness, sharp as a pain, rose inside him.

"Don't ask me to feel sorry for you, Miss Haines," he said bitingly. "Not after tonight. You wanted to strike at me and you have. You knew just how to do it, too, didn't you? You have all the necessary gifts—considerable allure, and shameless willingness to use it for cold-blooded ends."

"I wonder you have the nerve to talk to me about being cold-blooded—"

"I was doing my job!" he said harshly.

"Oh, yes, of course. You were doing it for money! That makes it better, doesn't it? The bigger the fee the better the cause. Did you get a nice fat fee for taking a scalpel and cutting my father into little pieces so that the newspapers could all have a bit to gloat over and the judge could have the rest? And have your fees gone up proportionately since? I do hope so. It would be a pity for you to turn yourself into an inhuman machine all for nothing."

He listened to this speech in silence. He might have turned to stone. Rae found herself almost wishing he'd lash out at her. Anything would have been better than this eerie stillness.... It was as though he were bleeding inside.

She'd expected rage and was ready to stand up to it. But his stunned face and deathly pallor gave her an uncomfortable feeling of guilt, as though she'd inflicted a mortal injury where she'd meant only to deal a blow. Into her mind came the sight of his face as they'd danced, unguarded, vulnerable to her. She tried to push the thought away. She couldn't afford it now. But suddenly her victory was ashes in her mouth.

She wanted never to see Giles Blake again, or to have to think about this night, which strangely hadn't turned out to be as enjoyable as she'd expected. She picked up her purse and turned to the door.

But Giles seemed to come to life as he saw her move. He took one step and barred her way.

"Where do you think you're going?" he said quietly.

"I'm leaving. I've done what I came to do. There's nothing to keep me here."

"Except that I want you to stay. You seem to forget that I've hired you for the evening. The clock hasn't struck midnight, Cinderella, and until it does you're bought and paid for."

"I'd have thought you'd had enough of my company," she said ironically.

"I told you I always get full value for money. So do you, evidently."

"What's that supposed to mean?"

"You've given me a fine tragic performance, but do you imagine that I can't use my eyes? You're not a victim, Miss Haines, you're a survivor. Your sort of woman always comes out on top, because you've got something men will pay money for—a lot of money, if that mink jacket is anything to go by.

She stared at him in disbelief. "Are you suggesting that I . . . ?"

"You were for hire, weren't you? There's a word for women who can be hired."

"You knew what the terms were."

"I know what the agency told me. But don't expect me to believe that you don't make 'private arrangements.' I know how your father's affairs were left, with every penny tied up in legal proceedings. You couldn't have salvaged any of his fortune, but you're not short of money now. That jacket cost a pretty penny. You're doing well, and so you should be. I congratulate you on fighting back. But let's not fool ourselves about how you did it."

In the silence, Rae folded her arms and looked up at him. Her head was tilted and her long, blond hair hung like a curtain. The eyes that met his were alight with laughter and the wry acceptance of defeat.

"Well, what the hell!" she said. "A woman has to make a living. I wasn't trained for anything. What else could I do?"

"Nothing, evidently," he said dryly. "At least you're honest. In fact, those are the first honest words you've uttered this evening."

She laughed up at him provocatively.

"Well?" she said. "Aren't you going to take me home?"

Suddenly he knew how very badly he wanted this disturbing woman. From his first sight of her, he had ached to possess her. Everything since then had been the prelude to this moment, and now it was here he was aware that he'd never meant the evening to end in any other way. At the same time he knew a sense of illogical dismay that she'd confirmed his worst opinion of her. Well, what had he expected? he wondered. Rae, watching him closely, saw his lip curl in an expression of unmistakable contempt but didn't know that it was directed at himself.

"Let's go," he said. "But to my place."

"Oh, no," she said quickly. "My place would be a much better idea. And I'd like you to see it—I really would." She looked up at him from beneath her lashes. "It's rather special. I shouldn't think you've ever seen anywhere quite like it."

"All right," he said. "Your place."

In a few minutes they were in the Rolls-Royce. Rae pulled her jacket warmly about her and said, "Head north. Then I'll direct you."

Fifteen minutes' driving brought them to the part of London where she lived. As Rae gave him directions, she could see Giles's brows contracted into a frown and guessed that the area wasn't what he'd expected.

"Turn left and we're there," she said.

At last, he pulled up outside the apartment block. He followed Rae out of the car and stood looking around him at the dereliction that could be seen even in this light. The moon picked out the mangled silhouettes of the car dump next door, a train rumbled nearby, and from the next street came the sound of someone kicking a tin can.

"What are you playing at?" he demanded. "You don't live in a place like this."

Rae didn't reply, but turned and headed for the entrance. Giles hurried after her.

"What's the idea of bringing me here?" he said, restraining her with a hand on her arm. She shook him off.

"You'll have all the answers when we get inside," she said. "We'll have to walk, I'm afraid, because the elevator is broken down again."

He walked beside her up the four flights of stairs. The lighting was poor. Lamps were fitted in each corner, but many of these had been smashed by vandals. As they turned the second landing, two shapes appeared on the landing above. Drunken laughter identified them as two young men, perhaps eighteen. Their faces lit up as they saw Rae, but fell as they perceived Giles's broad-shouldered presence. They scurried down, shouldering their way past.

Despite the poor light, Rae could see that Giles was taking in everything—the bare concrete stairs, the graffiti on the walls, the empty bottles left on the steps to the peril of the unwary, the smell of boiled cabbage and beer. He said nothing, but when she stopped at one of the doors, he faced her, and his eyes were full of cynicism that faded into incredulity as she fitted her key in the lock and turned it.

She went in ahead of him, switching on all the lights and throwing open the doors.

"Come in," she said. "Come and see the love nest, the fun palace. See what luxury my sinful earnings have brought me."

He entered with slow steps like a man dragging his way through a nightmare. His eyes roamed over the apartment, so tiny that even the most basic furniture made it look crowded. He noted mechanically that she was trying to economize on electricity by using low wattage bulbs in the lamps, so that the place had that depressed air that comes with poor lighting. But no gloom could hide the patch of damp that defied all efforts to dry it out, the bare space on the bathroom wall where no tiles would stick, the crack at the junction of two walls that she'd tried to fill herself.

Everything was spotlessly clean, though, bearing witness to her determination to maintain her own standards in the face of overwhelming odds. It was the desperate cleanliness of a woman fighting to keep her chin up.

Why had he thought of that phrase? He closed his eyes, and his mother's voice spoke in his mind, so loud and clear that it was as though she was there beside him.

You've got to keep your chin up. That's the only way to survive.

She'd said it often, as though reciting a spell to keep demons away. The demons had been numerous, starting with his father—when he was there. She'd said it with her nose bleeding after a clout from his father's fist. She'd said it when the electricity had been cut off because they couldn't pay the bill, and said it again when they were evicted.

She hadn't mentioned keeping their chins up when his father had vanished altogether because no one pretended that was a tragedy, but she'd intoned the ritual in the face of cold, rats, illness and even her own death.

She'd imbued him with her own conviction that nothing mattered but to get on and get out. With the help of his marvelous brain he'd made his escape and never looked back. But the memories were there whether he looked back at them or not. They drove him on and allowed him no pause for rest. They formed his worst nightmares, making him wake in the small hours, shaking with horror. They were with him now.

"How long have you lived here?" he asked at last in a stunned voice.

"Three years. I was lucky to get it."

"Lucky?"

"For the money I could afford to pay, yes. Besides, I'm single, and single people don't come high on the council's housing list, so we get what nobody else wants."

"I'm not surprised nobody wants it. It's a hellhole."

"I told you it was like nothing you'd ever seen before."

He looked at her coldly. "You deliberately led me on to expect something different."

"I didn't put any false ideas in your mind. *You* put them there. You'd decided I was a call girl, and no denial of mine would have convinced you. You had to see for yourself. Even you can hardly suspect me of entertaining clients in this little pavilion of pleasure."

"My God," he murmured softly, looking round him. "How did you come to this?"

"You already know the answer. As you said, I couldn't salvage anything of Andrew's, just a few personal things of my own. I lived on them for a while, but then they ran out. I work as a shorthand typist in a little construction firm. One evening a week I do hire work."

"But why only one evening a week?" he said. "You must be in demand. Surely if you did more escort work you could live better than this."

"Probably," she said with a shrug. "But one evening a week is all I can spare. I'm taking a degree with the Open University, and I need all my remaining time for studying."

"Studying what?"

"Economics. One legacy Andrew did manage to leave me was a good head for figures."

Now he understood the meaning of the shabby desk in the corner, with the books piled untidily on it. He pulled some of them toward him and looked at the titles: *Economics, Theory & Practice*, *Economics for Advanced Students.* Scattered over the desk were sheets of paper covered with figures in her firm hand.

"I take my finals in a few months," said Rae as she watched him. "With any luck I should pass. Then, it's goodbye to all this." She waved a hand at her surroundings. "I'm not asking for sympathy. As you said, I'm a survivor, although not quite in the way you meant. I can hang on till I've got my qualifications."

For the second time that evening Giles had the unnerving impression that time had slipped by. It was sixteen years ago and he was a law student struggling to survive on a tiny grant, living off tea and toast, hungry more often than not. He too had been forced to supplement his income in the evening, working till one in the morning in a restaurant kitchen and fighting to stay awake the next day. And always one thought had thrummed through his aching head: not much longer. *Hang on!*

He looked at Rae and found that she'd subtly altered as though someone had slid a colored filter over the light. Now she was like himself, part of the secret comradeship of those who wore out their youth in weary nights and gray dawns, their eyes fixed on the distant goal of "one day." For him "one day" had arrived, and until tonight he'd told himself that he was satisfied.

"It's an awful life," he said, half to himself. "Cold or tired or hungry—sometimes all three."

"True enough," she said. "But I don't need your sympathy."

"No, I can see that," he said, looking at her again. For the first time, he wondered if he'd been lucky to start with nothing, so that he'd grown up with the weapons for survival—endurance, hunger, desperation—always at hand. How would it be to grow up with everything, then find it all stripped away? Would he have managed any better than she had if he'd started "soft"? Would he have managed so well? Despite what she'd done to him, he felt the birth of a reluctant respect.

He turned back to the desk to replace the book he was still holding. As he did so, the pile of books slipped and scattered over the desk like a landslide. He picked them up and began to replace them, but Rae was there in a moment, saying, "I'll do it."

He left her to it, his attention drawn by something that had been partly obscured by the books. He was holding a large photograph of a handsome middle-aged man with a grizzled appearance. Beside him was a young girl of about seventeen. They were laughing at each other, and their wide, candid eyes made their faces uncannily alike. Giles was skilled at analyzing evidence; analyzing people came harder to him. But now, struggling to make his mind run on unfamiliar lines, he understood that Andrew Haines's childlike look had been the truth. One part of him had remained a child, with a child's innocence and amoral opportunism. It was the same part that had made him such an effective crook.

Giles looked at the picture more closely and realized that the likeness lay not only in the shape of their features, but also in the love that blazed between them. He'd seen that look once before, in a courtroom, when the laughter had died and only the love remained. He thought of his own eight-year-old daughter whom he'd last seen three weeks ago. He thought of the telephone conversation they'd had that morning, of her careful politeness barely concealing her embarrassment at having nothing to say to him, and he put the picture down abruptly.

"I was a fool to read so much into that jacket," he said in a curt voice to hide his emotion. "It looks like genuine mink, but I suppose it's a fake that you hired for the evening."

"No," she said. "It *is* genuine mink, and it's mine. My father gave it so me."

He stared at her. "Then what the devil are you doing with it? Do you know what you could get by selling it?"

"I've got a rough idea. But I'll never sell it. It was the last thing he ever gave me. You still haven't understood, have you? I *loved* my father. He may have been a crook to you, he was a wonderful father to me. If I was starving to death I wouldn't sell his last gift.

"Besides," she added with a shrug, "it's a useful accessory when I hire myself out to men who are incapable of attracting female company in the normal way."

She saw him wince and knew this had gone home. Suddenly she was desperately tired.

"Have you seen enough?" she asked.

"Yes," he said heavily. "I know now why you brought me here. I'm sorry, Tanis—"

"Rae," she said angrily.

"Rae—I'm sorry. I had no idea."

"No, for you the story ends when the trial's over. The rest of us—people in the dock and the witness box—we're just puppets for you to play your games with, aren't we? Only we're not. For us the story goes on. We have to live with what you've done to us."

"Rae, listen to me," he said urgently. "Try to understand something. Your father was guilty—"

"I know that. I'm not—"

"Let me finish. He did the things he was accused of, and whoever had prosecuted him, the result would have been much the same."

"They said your summing up was worth another two years on his sentence," she flung at him. "And I know why. If he was so plainly guilty then anyone could have prosecuted him and got a verdict. So you had to show you were more brilliant than the rest, didn't you?"

A shadow seemed to settle on his face. If she'd believed him capable of feelings she'd have thought he was ashamed.

"What I'm trying to tell you," he said after a while, "is that what happened to you would have happened, anyway. It isn't something that *I* did."

"You don't have to tell me that," she said. "I hate you for the way you behaved at the trial, not for what happened to me afterward. Tonight was for Andrew's sake, not mine. I wanted you to see this—" she flung out a hand at their depressing surroundings "—not because I blame you for it, but because you were so eager to write me off as a tramp, and I wasn't going to let you get off so easily. 'It's all right,' you'd have said to yourself, 'she turned out to be a tart, so what does it matter?' "

At these words, so uncanny an echo of his earlier thoughts, a dull flush appeared in his cheeks.

"Rae, for God's sake," he said harshly, "you've had your revenge. You've done everything you meant to. What more do you want? Apologies? Do you think I don't know you'd cast those back in my teeth?"

"You're right," she said wearily. "All I want now is for you to go."

"All right, I'll go—for now. But I'll be back."

"I don't want to see you again."

"Of course we must meet again. We can't leave matters here."

"Why not?"

"Because something's happened that you couldn't have expected. You've got your father's gift for planning ahead, but even you couldn't have planned that we should want each other."

"You're deluding yourself," she said coldly. "You're the last man I could want."

"Perhaps I'm the last man you ought to want, just as I'm probably crazy to want you after tonight, but it's there and it's useless to deny it."

She stared at him in disbelief.

"You didn't really think I was going to sleep with you, now or ever, did you?" she demanded. "I wouldn't let you touch me. There's nothing between us, Giles. Whatever you might have imagined, it was all part of the performance, like the wig."

His eyes glinted. "So you were just leading me on? When we danced and you melted against me, that was all pretense?"

"All pretense," she confirmed.

She turned away from him. Her sense of danger, so intense earlier in the evening, had deserted her now. She didn't see him come after her. She only felt the hands that turned her around and pulled her hard against him.

"It's not me that's deluded, Rae," he said, his mouth very close to hers. "You're the fool if you think you can turn the clock back and deny what's happened to us."

She tried to protest that nothing had happened, but the burning feel of his lips on hers told her she was wrong. His hand pressed into the small of her back made it impossible to escape him, and there was a shocking thrill in the sensation of the lean, hard body against the length of hers, willing her to respond. Heat flooded her, defying her mind's resistance. She writhed against him and managed to wrench her mouth free.

"You're mad," she muttered. "What are you trying to prove?"

"I'm trying to get you to face the truth, Rae. You started something tonight and now it has to go on to the finish. You weren't just pretending. No woman could pretend that much."

She'd have denied it if her lips had been free but he'd claimed them again, more insistently this time, urging them to part for him. She refused, yet somehow his tongue was flickering against the soft inner flesh of her mouth, sending forks of pleasure tingling through her. In his arms, her body seemed to waken after a long sleep, welcoming him with searing intensity, despite all she could do to deny him.

His hands were moving over her, their skilled movements calling forth a response that told her she'd been fooling herself all these years. She wasn't a cold woman, not if her enemy could make her ache for his caresses like this, as though her body existed only for him.

She must escape him soon or she'd come to grief. Her vibrant flesh beneath his hands would tell him all he wanted to know. For the second time that evening she had the sensation of being naked in his arms, but this time it was a thousand times more intense and terrifying. When he began to explore her, tracing the curves of her hips, her tiny waist, her breasts, she made a movement to push him away. But her limbs were weighted and it was as much as she could do to slide her arms about his neck.

She could feel him trembling as if with fever, and suddenly she knew an intense desire to touch him everywhere and discover what this strong man would become when passion had destroyed the last of his control. The impulse horrified her and she tried to force it down, but her mind persisted in wandering curiously over him, removing the sedate, formal clothing and revealing the male splendor beneath to her hungry senses.

He drew back far enough to say in a ragged voice, "We're not playing games now, either of us. The past's over, Rae. Forget it."

"I can't forget it," she said desperately. She wrenched herself free and moved away, trying to put a safe distance between them. But there was no safety from his eyes, which followed her, seeming to touch her with their heat.

"I can't forget it," she repeated. "I can't betray Andrew."

"For pity's sake, forget Andrew," he said harshly. "He's dead. You can't go on all your life being Andrew Haines's daughter."

"But I *am* Andrew Haines's daughter. I'm what he made me."

"That's not true, not anymore. Eight years ago you were what he made you, a pretty, useless little doll. Now you're a strong woman who's fought back with only her own courage to help her. *You* did that, not your father, and I admire you for it."

"And what I did to you tonight?" she said, looking him square in the face. "Did you admire that?"

She saw by the shock in his face that he'd forgotten it. She supposed that this moment was some kind of triumph for her, but she was too exhausted to care. All she felt was a desperate desire to make him leave.

Giles stared at her. Oblivious to everything but his passion, he'd been on the verge of saying that what she'd done tonight didn't matter. Nothing mattered except that they'd found each other, and he wouldn't let her go. But as the tumult in his blood subsided, something held him silent. Her eyes were looking up at him, wide, candid, transparently honest, and he remembered who else had had eyes like that, and who'd been a practiced deceiver. He felt like a man in a dream who wakes to find himself in an alien place.

Rae couldn't read his thoughts, but she saw his face stiffen suddenly.

"The past will never be over for us, Giles," she said. "You feel it, too. I really do want you to go. We've got nothing else to say to each other."

This time he didn't try to argue but headed straight for the door. Halfway down the stairs he told himself that he'd never see her again. He wanted to forget that she existed.

Four

The phone rang on Rae's desk. She gave an uncertain glance at the door of Frank Kinroy's office, but he seemed to be occupied. She snatched up the receiver.

"Rae?" It was Sally from the agency.

"Yes. Make it quick. Mr. Kinroy's here."

"Okay. I've got an urgent request for you this evening. Giles Blake has called and asked for you."

Rae drew in her breath and said firmly, "That's quite impossible, Sally. I'm booked for tomorrow, and you know I never work more than one night a week."

"Yes, I told him that, but he's very insistent that he wants you."

"Will you tell him please that I'm fully booked, now and in the future?"

"Oh! Does that mean he's an octopus?"

"Octopus" was the agency slang for a man who got out of hand. Once he'd been reported as "having eight arms," the agency never accepted another booking from him. Despite her frayed nerves, Rae couldn't help chuckling.

"No, he's not an octopus. It's personal."

It was three weeks since the night of the dinner. A silence had followed, lasting a week. Then Giles had telephoned her at home. She'd refused to see him again and put the phone down abruptly. The second time he'd called she replaced the phone at once, terrified for her hard-won peace. Now, it seemed, his ingenuity had found another way to reach out to her.

She hoped that this time he'd accept her decision as final. She didn't want to see Giles again, and especially she didn't want to think about him. He made her feel uneasy.

The memory of his arms around her and his mouth on hers had stayed with her, defying all attempts to banish them. She told herself that she'd betrayed Andrew by giving in to a momentary weakness, but the edge of her guilt was blunted by the memory of Andrew himself laughing and refusing to condemn any human frailty, his own, least of all. She knew in her heart that her father would have forgiven her for the events of that night. The person who could not forgive her was herself.

But her dissatisfaction had another cause, one she couldn't give a name to, except that it had to do with the horror on his face when he'd seen where she lived. She had the shaming suspicion that she'd struck a defenseless man, although why she should think of Giles as defenseless was a mystery to her.

The next evening she put on the second of her two "stage costumes," a black cocktail dress, fitted on the red wig and went to meet her client for the evening. Sam Rogers was a provincial business man in London for dinner given by his firm's head office. He'd been a widower for a year and knew no one in London.

Rae had agreed to meet him in the lobby of his hotel at seven o'clock. Sam turned out to be a large, red-faced man of about fifty, with the manner of a boisterous puppy and a loud laugh.

"Well, now, this is nice," he said when they met in the hotel bar. "Let's sit down a moment, shall we? We've time for a drink before we have to be off. What'll you have?"

Rae asked for orange juice and Sam laughed.

"*That's* no good! This is an evening out. We're going to enjoy ourselves. Waiter, double whisky for me and gin and tonic for the lady."

Rae bit her lip, then managed to force a smile. Sam Rogers was looking her up and down with an appreciative gleam in his eye.

"Well, I will say they did me proud," he said at last. "I told that agency I wanted a real smasher—had to leave it to them to choose, you see. But get me a corker, I said—a girl who'll knock their eyes out. By God, you will and all! You and me are going to get on really well."

"Of course we are, Sam," she said politely.

The waiter served their drinks. Sam signed the bill and exclaimed over the price.

"Highway robbery, if you ask me," he boomed. "But why should I care? It's all going on expenses."

"What about me?" she said mischievously. "Will I appear on your expenses, too?"

She immediately regretted her little joke because Sam threw his head back and roared with laughter. Heads turned in their direction, and she gave silent thanks that the bar lighting was dim.

"Hey that's a good one," he said, subsiding into noisy hiccups. "Put you on expenses. I should just think not. Oh, Lord that's rich...."

He was laughing again. Rae ground her teeth and looked surreptitiously around the bar to see if they were attracting much attention. Then she stiffened with horror and wished the earth could open and swallow her up.

Giles was sitting at a nearby table, looking at her. For a moment their eyes met, his hard and watchful, hers filled with dismay. Then she turned away defiantly.

"We ought to be going soon, Sam," she said. "Don't we have to be there by eight o'clock?"

"Plenty of time, plenty of time. I want you to myself a little longer." he gave a whiskey chuckle directly into her face. "Drink up. That gin cost good money, even if it wasn't mine."

"But I really don't want it. I'd have preferred orange juice—"

"Oh, come on, let your hair down. Here—" His voice had grown petulant. He picked up the glass and pushed it into her hand. Rae's mouth tightened and she tried to edge away from him, but she was wedged into a corner and the only way out was past him. Sensing her resistance, Sam slid his free arm around her shoulders. Her cheeks flamed at the thought of Giles witnessing this undignified scene.

"Look, I've got an idea," he said, breathing fumes over her, "why don't we give the 'do' a miss and just stay here?"

"We can't do that," she said firmly. "What would your boss say?"

"What can he say? I was sick, wasn't I? I've really taken to you—"

"I'm sorry, Sam, but the agreement was that I attend this dinner with you—"

"Ah, but if I say I'm not going, what can you do?" He chuckled. "Now look, why don't we—"

"Good evening, Rae."

In her agitation, Rae hadn't noticed Giles approaching their table. Now she looked up to find him standing over them. Sam's jaw had dropped. It dropped farther when Giles settled himelf into the chair opposite.

"Look, this is a private party," he began. "No strangers."

"Oh, but I'm not a stranger," said Giles smoothly. "Rae and I are old friends. We've known each other for about eight years, haven't we, Rae? Why don't you introduce me?"

She ground her teeth. "Giles, this is Sam Rogers a...a friend of mine. Sam, this is Giles Blake, a distant acquaintance who is just leaving. I'm afraid I can't ask you to join us tonight, Giles. As Sam says, this is a private party."

"You mean you *want* to be alone with him?" said Giles, raising a sardonic eyebrow in Sam's direction and making no attempt to hide his contempt for the other man.

Rae glared at him and turned her head to speak out of the side of her mouth.

"Please go away," she hissed. "I'm perfectly all right."

"I don't think you are," said Giles, also turning his head so that Sam was excluded.

"I don't need your help!"

"Nonsense! I'm not leaving you alone with this oaf...."

"Here, here..." Sam protested, unheeded by anybody.

"He's turning nasty already. What do you think he'll be like by the end of the evening?"

"I'm not standing for this—" Sam began to bluster.

Giles seemed to become aware of him again.

"Look, Sam" he said in a genial voice in which the deadly undertone was clearly audible, "why don't we talk business? You've made a bad bargain tonight. You thought you were buying a tart and you've discovered that you were wrong. We all make mistakes, and the best thing to do is cut your losses. Otherwise I'll be forced to break your nose, and that might spoil your evening, besides being difficult to explain to the boss."

"But I've paid good money," Sam howled.

"Well, this should cover it." Giles tossed some notes onto the table. "That's twice the agency fee and you've still time to pick up a real tart, or get legless, whichever suits you best. Now if you'll excuse us—"

He rose and pulled out the heavy table, guiding Rae out with his hand. She stared at him indignantly. But when she looked back at Sam, her enthusiastic host was thumbing through the notes, his eyes gleaming as he realized that he'd made a profit.

"Good night Sam," she said through gritted teeth.

"Night." He didn't even look up.

"My car's just outside," said Giles as he led her out of the bar. His hand was still on her arm as though to prevent her escape, but she had no intention of running away. She had plenty she wanted to say to Giles.

"Just what did you think you were doing back there?" she demanded when they were in the Rolls and heading north. "Playing St. Giles and the dragon? How *dare* you—" She became speechless with anger.

Perhaps Giles had the wisdom to let her rage run its course, or perhaps he was merely concentrating on the traffic. At any rate, he didn't make the mistake of answering.

"Do you think that's the first troublesome customer I've ever had?" she fumed. "Do you think I don't know how to deal with them?"

"You didn't look as if you did," he said mildly.

"If things had got worse I could have left. But it doesn't usually come to that. If you're firm enough the first—"

"Spare me the agency handbook," he interrupted. "Another few drinks and he'd have been right out of control, and you know it. If it hadn't been for your fee, you'd have been glad of some help."

"If it wasn't for my fee, I wouldn't have been there in the first place," she snapped.

"Do you need it so badly?" he said quietly after a moment.

"Only for another six months. Then I'll be free of men like that."

"Unless one of them's harmed you in the meantime," he said angrily. "Do you ever think of that?"

"Of course I do. But that kind of thing doesn't happen very often. Mostly they're meek, shy little men who wouldn't say boo to a goose."

They drove on in silence until she broke it by quoting wryly, "'Of all the bars in all the world, why did you have to come to that one?'"

"It wasn't an accident," he said. "I came to your home tonight. I arrived just as you were getting into your minicab. So I followed."

"Spying on me!" she said, incensed.

"I was concerned for you—and rightly so, as it happens."

"How can I convince you that I don't need a bodyguard?"

"How can I convince *you* that what you're doing is thoroughly dangerous?"

"That's for me to decide. Look, Mr. Blake—"

"It was Giles earlier in the evening."

"Only for the benefit of our audience. As far as I'm concerned, you're Mr. Blake and I'm Miss Bonham."

"What happened to Tanis Haines?"

"Tanis Haines was destroyed in the witness box eight years ago," she said bitterly. "After that she crawled out of sight. Rae Bonham was my mother's name."

He said nothing, but when she looked at him a moment later, his knuckles were white on the steering wheel.

At last, he drew up outside her door and switched off the engine.

"May I come inside?" he said. "There are things I want to say."

"All right," she said reluctantly.

When they were inside her front door, she said, "Go in the front room. I'll be with you in a moment."

She hurried into the bedroom and changed the black dress for jeans and sweater. The red wig went back in its box and she brushed out her own hair before tying it back severely. Finally she cleaned off every last scrap of makeup.

Giles was standing at her desk flicking through one of her books when she returned. He looked up as she came in and his eyes widened at the sight of her.

"This is off duty," she said, misunderstanding his look.

She didn't know that with her face bare and her hair tied back like a schoolgirl she looked years younger. For any man, the transformation would have been startling, but for Giles it was as though the years had vanished and he saw the eighteen-year-old Tanis again. But this time, instead of the "spoiled rich brat" he saw only the vulnerability and innocence, and wondered how he could have missed them before.

"Tanis—" he said involuntarily.

"My name is Rae," she reminded him. "I'll make us some coffee."

He stood in the doorway of the kitchen as she got to work, and said, "How are you coping with the work?"

"Well enough, according to my tutor. It's a lot harder in the final year. But he says he thinks I'll pass."

"And then what?"

"Then I start writing around for a job."

"You know it's not just a matter of passing but how well you pass. The better firms want a first class degree. Without that you'll end up in some dump where you'll be little better off than you are now."

This was her secret fear, but she only said, "I'll manage."

"Will you? Have you looked at yourself recently? You've got black smudges under your eyes. You're working into the small hours, aren't you? When do you sleep?"

"I sleep all right," she snapped edgily. In fact, she'd nodded off over her books the night before, and woken a couple of hours later, cold and stiff, with barely enough time to get to work. She'd been dozy all day and now, just when she needed all her wits about her, she felt her mind fuzzing over.

"You shouldn't have come here," she said.

"I had to. It was the only way to see you."

"Don't you ever give up?"

"Not when it's important."

"Giles, I haven't changed about anything. Things are just as we left them three weeks ago."

His mind went back to himself that night, leaving this apartment, determined to mistrust Andrew Haines's daughter and forget her. He thought of the restless week that had followed, the constant hope that today she'd cease to trouble him, the growing understanding that the only way to forget her was to see her just once more.

"Will you listen to me?" he said now. "I've been thinking a lot these past few weeks. I told you I admire you. I admire the struggle you're putting up. I know exactly what you're going through. I went through the same myself." He saw her raise one eyebrow in hilarious disbelief, and his temper began to rise.

"Look," he snapped, nettled, "last time I was here you said you didn't like me jumping to glib conclusions about you. The same goes for me. You seem convinced that I'm incapable of understanding how you have to live, but I was brought up in slums next to which this would be paradise. When I began studying for the bar I had just my student grant and nothing else, and that grant isn't designed to be lived on. It's supposed to supplement an allowance from your parents, but my mother could as easily have flown to the moon as given me an allowance. So I lived on that grant and I damned near died on it. I know what it's like to freeze because you can't afford to turn the heating on, and to have to decide whether to eat a sandwich at midday or save it till the evening, and—" he stopped abruptly.

"Yes, well," he went on after a moment, coloring slightly, "that's neither here nor there."

He wondered what ailed him that he couldn't be in her company for five minutes without losing his usual self-control. It had been the work of years to perfect it. It had enabled him to face crises in his personal life and the occasional failure in his professional life with scarcely a flicker to show that he cared. But Rae Bonham could destroy this laboriously perfected control as easily as if it was a cobweb.

Rae was looking at him curiously.

"So that's why," she said at last. "That explains what you did to my father. He was your ticket out, wasn't he?"

"I wasn't exactly a beginner even then," he said tersely. "If I hadn't already been a few rungs up the ladder, I wouldn't have been given that prosecution."

"But after that trial you jumped clear over the next few rungs, didn't you?" she said.

"Can we get back to the matter at hand?" he said in a hard voice. "I came here to say I want to help you."

"Help me? How?"

"Financially at first, and later through people I know. I want you to let me give you enough to live on while you study for your finals. You'll be able to give up your daytime job, and you won't have to do any more escort work. You can spend your whole time studying. If you pass well, I can introduce you to a good firm I know."

He stopped because Rae was staring at him with an expression on her face that he couldn't read. The only certain thing was that it expressed neither gratitude nor pleasure.

"You're not serious?" she said at last. "You actually expect me to take your money?"

"Rae, you *need* money. You can't go on like this."

"That isn't your problem," she said firmly.

"I'd like to make it my problem. I want to help you."

"Why? You said the other night that what's happened to me wasn't your fault. So why should you help me?"

"Because I *want* to. I told you I've been through this myself. That's reason enough."

She shook her head. "It's no reason at all. I don't want your money, Giles, nor do I want you pulling strings among your connections. You're not going to buy yourself an easy conscience on the cheap."

"For the last time—I have nothing on my conscience," he said. "Your father was a crook and I prosecuted him."

"You didn't prosecute him, you savaged him. You went for his jugular and then you went for mine, for good measure. You weren't trying to secure justice. You were aiming to impress your legal friends."

She saw his mouth tighten, but he said nothing, only turned away from her into the room. She brought the coffee out and set it on the table.

"Look," she said in a gentler tone, "why don't you just go away? You meant well, but it wouldn't work. I couldn't live off you."

Where were the words that would persuade her? he wondered. Like a magician vainly seeking to recapture old spells, he called on his polished tongue to help him and found it was silent.

"I think perhaps you've misunderstood," he said at last. "I wouldn't ask anything from you. There'd be no strings. We wouldn't even have to see each other again. I should have made that clear from the start."

"It makes no difference. I won't—*can't*—live off you. It's impossible."

"Because of your father?"

"Among other things, yes."

"You know what he'd say to you if he could hear us now, don't you? He'd say 'Take it. Bleed the swine of everything you can get, and good luck.'"

This was so exactly what Andrew would have said that she was surprised by a gasp of laughter. It was out before she could deny it, and she looked at him with resentment. He had no right to understand Andrew so astutely and to turn that understanding against her.

"Yes, well," she muttered, "Andrew believed in getting the last penny, I admit."

"And he didn't care how or from whom. He'd have had no sympathy with this puritan standoffishness. Reparation, not retribution, would have been his motto."

She ground her teeth, not caring for the turn the conversation was taking.

"You seem to forget that I had a mother, too," she said. "I'm not a replica of Andrew. I have my own standards, and they're not always his."

"And one of them is 'never forgive,' isn't it?" he said bitterly.

"What did you expect? Did you really think I was going to shrug my shoulders and say 'Oh, well, as long as he's paying me money, everything's all right'?"

"Rae, listen to me. If you won't live off me—well, I understand that. I respect it. But I want you to give up escort work. Let me give you enough to cover your weekly fee, just so you don't have to risk yourself with oafs like Sam Rogers again."

Her chin set in a stubborn line. "Can't you understand? I don't want to take anything from you."

He swore violently and turned away from her, slamming one fist into the other. Her immovability made him want to smash something. For three weeks, he'd thought of her in the company of men picked at random, men she knew nothing about. He'd thought of the swing of her hips, the soft curves of her mouth and the aura of feminity that enveloped her like perfume, and he'd known that in a man's company she was tempting danger in ways that she couldn't comprehend. Whatever she said, he knew it was vital to protect her safety. He told himself that he owed her that.

"Will you listen to reason?" he said at last. "I'm offering you the chance to escape from men like Sam Rogers. All right, all right, you could have taken care of yourself. But can you pretend you were enjoying it?"

"No," she said at once. "Those evenings are no fun."

"Well, then—"

"But they're my independence. They're not charity. I keep my own head above water and I do it without help."

"What kind of woman does work like that if she doesn't have to?" he snapped.

"The kind of woman you made me," she flung back. "I owe you a vote of thanks for that. I can put up with all sorts of things now because you gave me my first lesson in endurance, and it was a very thorough one."

He stopped as if she'd struck him.

"You won't let me help you at all," he said slowly. "You won't accept the slightest thing from me. You must hate me much more than I'd realized." He paused, then said in a bleak tone, "Since that's the case, there's something you might like to hear. Do you know what a Queen's Counsel is?"

She frowned. "Yes, it's something advocates become if they're good enough."

"That's right. You apply to the Lord Chancellor for an appointment as Queen's Counsel. If you get it, you can put the letters QC after your name and—well, very little else happens, but it's a sort of sign that you've arrived. Not everyone gets it, and very few get it the first time they apply. I wanted to be one of those few. I dare say that seems a trivial ambition to you, but it meant a lot to me.

"I made my first application this year and it was on the cards that I'd get it. But lawyers are a very conservative crowd, and after your performance the other night in front of half the top legal men in London I've heard, unofficially, that my appointment will probably be deferred 'to let the dust settle.' There's no knowing when I'll get it—or if I ever will. So you see, your revenge has been more successful than you could possibly have hoped. Good night, Tanis."

Five

Rae glared at the door of Frank Kinroy's office and subsided into her seat with a pile of freshly typed letters in her hand.

"Drat the man!" she muttered. "I wish he'd sign the letters when I've typed them. He knows I want to go."

"Do you think perhaps he just enjoys being difficult?" said Joan.

"There's no perhaps about it. He's had time to sign these twice over but suddenly he's 'too busy.'"

"And you want to get home to start studying, don't you?" said Joan sympathetically. "How's it going?"

Joan was the fellow typist whose innocent remark had started Rae off on the road to a degree. Since then, she'd taken a lively interest. She was in her mid-thirties, with a warm heart and a wry, unsentimental sense of humor. Over several years together at Kinroy & Son, the two women had developed the camaraderie of shared affliction.

"It's going all right, when I can concentrate on it," said Rae. "But Mr. Kinroy seems to take pleasure in making life difficult."

"Of course he does! He's stuck in this dump and doesn't like anyone else having the chance to get out."

"But Kinroy & Son is *his* dump," Rae objected. "He's the boss."

"Yes, but boss of what? It's still a dump."

"You don't mean he's actually trying to stop me from passing my exams?" said Rae, frowning.

"No, he's not bright enough to think of that. Mind you, I don't say he'd be heartbroken if you failed, but I think it's more general spite and jealousy that you're going to escape and he isn't."

Frank Kinroy opened his door.

"You can come in now," he said curtly.

He was a tubby man in late middle age with thinning hair and a halfhearted mustache. He had tiny gleaming eyes and a prissy mouth, too small for a man, which accurately reflected his mean-spirited, bullying nature.

He lingered over the letters Rae put before him, reading every one through slowly, though her working day was supposed to end at five-thirty and it was already five-forty. When he was unable to find anything wrong, he made a small displeased sound and signed them.

"I've got an important new client coming at one o'clock tomorrow," he said, "so I do hope you two will have your desks tidy. In fact, that applies to the whole office. He's got to walk through there, and I don't want him seeing the place looking like a mess. He wants an extension for his house. Let's put our best foot forward, eh?"

Rae, who was always impeccably tidy, ground her teeth but managed a smile.

"All right, you can go now. Make sure you mail these on your way home."

She dashed from the office and spent the next few minutes frantically licking the flaps on the envelopes, helped by Joan. One word repeatedly thrummed through her head—escape; escape from Frank Kinroy's petty bullying, indigestion from snatched, inadequate meals, constant weariness; escape from all that. Just a few months to go. Hang on!

Then she remembered that she'd been offered escape and had turned it down. As she hurried to the mailbox in the rain, she wondered if she was mad. Would it have been so very wrong to have accepted Giles's help? Andrew would certainly have told her to. Giles had been right about that. But her own stubborn pride wouldn't let her.

Giles lived in her mind as he'd been at their second meeting ten days earlier, at the moment when he'd told her how successful her revenge had been. Rae wondered how much he really minded. There'd been no sign in his steady voice to show that he was hurt or dismayed. His face had been blank as he'd spoken of the dashing of his most cherished hopes, carefully blank now that she'd thought of it.

She recalled his words: "I was brought up in slums next to which this would be paradise." They'd taken her by surprise; he'd seemed to her so much at one with his luxurious background. She'd even tried to dismiss the words as pure effect, but found she couldn't. Giles might be arrogant and ruthless, but he had standards of rigid honesty below which he wouldn't allow himself to fall. She didn't know how she knew this except that in some mysterious way she'd acquired an intimate knowledge of him.

Besides, there'd been conviction in his voice as he spoke of the hardships of studying on a pittance. Only a man who'd lived through it could have known what he did. Suddenly she realized that, out of everyone she knew, Giles was the only person who had the slightest idea what she was going through. It was disconcerting to feel a sense of fellowship with him.

The next day, she and Joan hurriedly tidied the office.

"Though why we bother I can't think," said Joan. "Important client, my foot! If he's worth anything, he wouldn't be wasting his time here."

"Well, I'm going to miss him, whoever he is," said Rae. "I'll be at lunch then, and I expect he'll be gone when I return."

At lunchtime she did some hurried shopping and dashed back to the firm. Frank Kinroy had eagle eyes where timekeeping was concerned. She reached her desk, breathless and flushed, at quarter to two. To her relief, the door to Mr. Kinroy's office was closed.

"The tea's just brewed," said Joan sympathetically. "Sit down and I'll pour you one."

Rae collapsed thankfully into her seat and accepted a cup.

"Has he asked for me?" she said in a low voice.

"No, Mr. Blake's still there. *Careful!* Now look what you've done! You've got tea all over you."

"What name did you say?" said Rae, mopping frantically at her dress.

"Giles Blake. He got here just after you left. Why, do you know him?"

"I know someone by that name, but I can't think of any reason for him to be here," said Rae untruthfully. "It must be someone else."

"What does your Giles Blake look like?"

"Tall, dark, mid-thirties—"

"Good-looking?"

"He's all right," said Rae grudgingly.

"Must be the same one," said Joan with a cheeky grin. "This one's 'all right,' too. Do you think it could be your Giles Blake?"

"He isn't *my* Giles Blake."

"Why are you going pink, then?"

"I'm not."

A buzzer went on the desk, and Mr. Kinroy's voice barked, "Is anyone bringing that tea in here?"

"Just coming!" Joan sang back.

"I'll take it," said Rae firmly.

"That's right. Go and see if it's him."

Rae took a deep breath. "That is *not* the reason. Oh, give me the tray."

It was him, of course. She knew that even before she opened the door and saw him sitting there, his handsome head bent over some plans on Mr. Kinroy's desk. He gave her the briefest glance before moving back to let her place the cups on the desk.

"This is my secretary, Miss Bonham," said Mr. Kinroy in a smooth voice he kept for his better-off customers.

Giles nodded and murmured a polite greeting. Nothing in his manner betrayed that he'd ever set eyes on Rae before. Rae, who'd been prepared to be outraged if he'd greeted her as an old friend and so drawn attention to her was illogically nettled.

"Now, shall we go over what we've agreed on so far?" said Mr. Kinroy, in an obsequious tone. "Miss Bonham, please stay and take notes."

In a moment she was seated, notebook on her knee, pencil at the ready. Her manner was as formal and correct as Giles's own. There was no sign of her inner disturbance. No one could have detected that her heart had leaped at the sight of him and hadn't yet resumed its normal sedate rhythm.

She kept her attention on her notebook, only raising her head slightly when Mr. Kinroy searched for words. But even this was disastrous as her eyes fell on Giles's hands resting calmly on the papers. They were large, shapely hands, long-fingered but muscular. She hadn't looked closely at them before, but she knew them well because their touch was still burned into her skin. She knew the feel of their intimate caresses evoking sensations deep within her that brought her body to life. Most of all, she knew an aching longing to feel them again.

"Have you got that, Miss Bonham?"

"I . . . I'm sorry, Mr. Kinroy. Would you repeat the last few words?"

He did so with a sigh of exaggerated patience.

"Okay, read it back to me," he said brusquely.

She did so, and her eyes widened as she took in the details that she'd noted down in shorthand while her mind was elsewhere. Giles intended to commission a twenty-foot room to be added onto his house.

She thought of his home, a huge empty mausoleum in which he lived alone since his wife and children had gone. She thought of what Frank Kinroy would charge him for this, and it was all she could do to stop herself staring at him in bewilderment.

"Type this up at once, please," said Mr. Kinroy. "Mr. Blake wants a copy to take with him."

When she returned with the copy a few minutes later, Giles was rising and collecting his things together.

"You'll come and look the place over Saturday, then?" he was saying to Frank Kinroy. "We'll settle the final details then. Thank you." These last words were addressed to Rae, who handed him the paper. He spoke with perfect courtesy but didn't meet her eyes.

"All right," Frank Kinroy snapped at her. "Don't hang around. Haven't you got any work to get on with?"

He ushered Giles out himself. Rae sat at her typewriter, aware of Joan's curious gaze, refusing to look up. She was struggling with her confused feelings. There was the old sense of danger back again, stronger than ever, annoyance that he wouldn't accept her word as final, and irritation at the arrogance that made him continually intrude on her life. She mulled over them for a long time, trying to ignore the fact that running beneath them all, half hidden but insistent, was the disturbing throb of relief.

He telephoned her at eight o'clock that evening. She waited half a minute before answering so that he wouldn't guess she'd been sitting by the phone.

"What do you think you're doing?" she demanded in a fair assumption of exasperation.

"I'm having an alteration made to my property."

"An alteration that you don't need and which is going to cost you thousands. He'll rook you on the price, and the work will be shoddy."

"Well, it should please you greatly to see me get my comeuppance. After all, you believe I'm living on blood money, don't you?"

She was silent. She couldn't answer.

"Giles, please," she said at last, "I don't want to see you taken for a ride."

"You know better than that, Rae. I'm no blue-eyed innocent to be fooled by a man of Kinroy's type. Whatever the price, I came prepared to pay it. Tell me something. Is he always as much of a vulgar little bully as he seemed this afternoon?''

"Not really. He puts it on a bit when he wants to impress a client. He thinks it makes him sound like a tycoon."

"Dear God! When I think of you having to work for such a man! Won't you see sense and let me help you?"

"No, I can't change my mind about that."

"Then I'll have to go on with the extension. That way at least I can keep my eye on you and make sure you're all right."

"How did you know where I worked?"

"I accidentally came across one of your pay slips when I was last in your apartment. I was flicking through the books on your desk while you were changing."

A silence fell between them. She felt she ought to hang up.

"Did you have any trouble from the escort agency over Sam Rogers?" he said at last.

"No. I was afraid he might have complained, but he hadn't. He couldn't, really. By giving him twice what he'd paid, you left him without a leg to stand on." Chagrin infused her voice. "I suppose I ought to thank you."

She heard him give a brief laugh. "No, don't do that. It might choke you."

"Yes, it might," she conceded, laughing.

"Do you have any other bookings?"

"Yes, my next one's agreed."

"I wish you wouldn't," he said emphatically.

"We've been over this. My answer's the same."

"Rae—" He broke off.

"Yes?" she said at last.

"Nothing. Good night."

She replaced the receiver and sat looking at it for a long time. She wondered if she could put the second bar of the electric heater on. She felt suddenly cold.

February passed into March and the bitter cold gave way to strong winds. Life in the office became more pleasant as Frank Kinroy learned how well he was going to do out of the extension to Giles's house, and his mood improved accordingly. Not that the work was without problems. Giles seemed to be oddly indecisive, always changing his mind about some previously agreed detail. Each alteration necessitated a visit to the office to mull over new plans with Mr. Kinroy, who privately rubbed his hands at the way the bill was mounting. It gave Rae a strange feeling when she discovered how much money Giles was throwing away on her account.

He never denied that it *was* on her account. His visits to the office were always impersonal. She might have been any secretary for all the attention he paid her. But each Friday night he telephoned her to inquire politely how she was. She might have thought that these calls, too, were impersonal if he hadn't once mentioned that she'd seemed tired the last time he was in the office. She knew then that he was secretly studying her looks and keeping watch over her.

With four months to go till her final exams, she became frantic, studying till the early hours night after night and rising heavy eyed in the morning. The fear of passing only moderately well began to haunt her. She tried to increase her working hours, but found she wasn't taking anything in. She began to grow desperate. Black smudges appeared under her eyes, and the face that looked back from her mirror had become almost haggard.

One Friday, she sat at her typewriter all through lunchtime, trying to keep up with a pile of letters. Frank Kinroy had left a mountain of correspondence till the last minute, and she knew he was going to demand that it all be done before she left that night. It was no use her protesting that the backlog was his own fault and she was entitled to leave at five-thirty. She'd done that once before, and received the reply that if she didn't like the job there were others she could try.

In a moment of rebellion she considered letting him fire her. Mentally she calculated the state benefits she'd be entitled to. They might just be enough to survive on. But some stubborn inner core of pride refused to consider living off the state. It was as unthinkable as living off Giles Blake.

Strangely, this, too, was Andrew's legacy. Andrew, who would have unhesitatingly advised her to squeeze the last penny from Giles, would have frowned if she'd taken unemployment benefits. To him it would have meant lack of initiative, the worst of all crimes in his books. As her fingers automatically pounded the keys, her mind went back to an argument they'd once had.... He'd never been able to see that not everyone was like himself.... There were thousands of little people who needed help, but like many strong, independent characters, he'd had no sympathy with them.... In fact, he'd hardly known that little people existed as individuals.... Why should she think of that now?

She wasn't sure when her fingers had slowed down, but they were made of lead suddenly, and the typewriter had grown enormous and started up off the desk to thump her on the forehead. But instead of being hard it turned into a soft pillow into which she could sink....

"Rae, wake up!"

Someone was shaking her, and she wished they'd stop because she was deliciously comfortable and didn't want to be disturbed. But the hands on her shoulders tightened and shook her harder.

"Wake up!" commanded a voice in her ear.

Some note or urgency in that voice pierced the fuzz that enveloped her. She opened her eyes and found herself looking straight into Giles's face.

"Rae!" he said in a low voice.

"What...?"

"You fell asleep over your typewriter. Luckily, Kinroy's door's closed. Try to wake up properly before he sees you. You know how he'll carry on if he guesses you fell asleep."

That thought spurred her to rub her eyes and try to make herself more alert.

"That's better," he said, looking at her and still talking quietly. "Now go and tell Kinroy I'm here. As soon as I'm in there, go and splash your face with cold water."

She did as he said. As the water brought her mind to life again, she sent up a prayer of gratitude to whichever kindly fate had made Giles walk in just then. If Frank Kinroy had discovered her asleep, he'd have outdone even himself in spiteful sarcasm, and she knew she couldn't have coped with it at the moment.

When she returned to the office, Joan was back from lunch and Mr. Kinroy's door stood open, showing the room to be empty.

"They went off for a drink," said Joan. "With any luck, it'll be an hour before Kinroy gets back. I'm beginning to like your Giles Blake."

She emphasized "your" very faintly and gave Rae a hopeful look, but Rae said nothing.

Frank Kinroy returned alone at four o'clock, breathing beer fumes and bonhomie. He even signed the letters Rae set in front of him without lingering over them. She began to cross her fingers.

But at five he called her back in and said, "I've just remembered a couple of things," and proceeded to dictate for half an hour.

"There's not too much there," he said when he'd finished. "You'll dash those off in no time. I'll still be here to sign them. I've got to catch up after that lunch hour."

It took her until seven to finish the letters, and it was seven-fifteen before he'd signed them.

"Put them in the mail on your way home," said Mr. Kinroy.

"I'm afraid I won't be able to," said Rae, controlling her temper. "We've run out of stamps, and the post office is shut."

"Run out of stamps? How did that happen?"

"There's no money in the petty cash. I did ask you for some, but you forgot."

"Well, couldn't you have bought some yourself? I'd have refunded you the money."

"I couldn't afford to buy them myself," said Rae, mentally adding, and you'd have taken six weeks to refund the money.

"If that's a hint for a raise I'm afraid it's fallen on stony ground," said Frank Kinroy with a smile that didn't reach his eyes. "Honestly, anyone would think I'm made of money. Oh, well, these will have to go on Monday, then. Luckily they're not urgent."

Rae got out quickly. It was raining outside but she didn't even stop to put her coat on first, because if she'd stayed a moment longer she'd have committed murder.

The office door led to a small yard filled with builders' clutter. On a winter evening it was dangerous because Frank Kinroy was too cheap to light it properly. As Rae picked her way carefully across in the darkness, she muttered furiously, "Four months, just four months. Then I can bury an ax in his head. And after that, I'll tell him what he can do with his damned job!"

The rain was pelting down, driven slantways by the gusting wind. At the entrance to the yard, she stopped and looked farther down the road. Even at this distance, she could see that there was a long line at her bus stop. Her spirits sank even lower as she began to plod onward. She didn't see the car that caught up with her and slowed to a crawl so it kept pace with her steps. Her head bent against the wind, she knew nothing until a sharp toot on a horn made her turn sharply. At that same moment, she realized that she'd always known he'd be here.

"Get in," said Giles. "I'll take you home. No, in the back." He reached over and opened the rear door of the Rolls. "You can stretch out back there."

She eased her way thankfully into the back seat.

"I'm all wet," she said. "I'll make a mess of your upholstery."

But even as she said it, the wide rear seat seemed to hypnotize her, inviting her to lie down on it. In another moment, she'd done so, and the outside world ceased to exist.

She was woken by a hand shaking her gently. A voice above her head said, "Wake up. We're here."

She hauled herself into a sitting position, but her head drooped and her eyes remained closed. Still half-asleep, she mumbled, "You shouldn't park here. We're not used to Rolls-Royces in this area. You'll be lucky if someone doesn't steal your wheels."

Giles's voice, with a hint of amusement, said, "I don't think the car's in any danger where it is. Come along."

She let him help her out. The effort of standing forced her awake, and she opened her eyes and looked around her.

"Where am I?" she said.

"Surely you recognize it. You've been here before."

"You said you were going to take me home."

"I meant *my* home. Did I forget to mention that?"

"Yes, you did," she said, trying to be indignant at his duplicity.

"I thought we could have dinner, and then I'll drive you to your place afterward."

Waves of sleep were still washing over her brain.

"I don't think—" she began. "That is, I'm really grateful for this afternoon but that doesn't mean—"

"Why don't we talk about it inside?" said Giles gently.

Suddenly it seemed like a very good idea. The front door was opened for them by the middle-aged woman Rae remembered seeing from her first visit to Giles's home. As soon as the door was shut behind them, Giles said, "Mrs. Jones, this is Miss Bonham, who'll be staying for dinner. But first I think she'd like a rest. Will you please show her upstairs?" He turned to Rae. "You can finish dozing and come down when you're ready. Dinner will wait for you."

Mrs. Jones was giving Rae a puzzled look, as if trying to associate this pale, rain-soaked blonde with the glossy redhead who'd arrived under the same name several weeks ago. But she said nothing as she showed Rae upstairs and along a corridor. At last she opened a white-painted door and showed Rae into a cheerful room with a single bed, covered with a pink counterpane. She indicated a hanger behind the door, and departed.

Rae just managed to stay awake long enough to hang up her dress. Then she slipped between the sheets and sank into a blissful sleep.

It was an hour later, when Giles made his way quietly into the room. The small bedside lamp was still on, throwing a soft, rosy glow over Rae's face, and her arm was stretched toward it, as though she'd fallen asleep in the act of trying to switch it off.

He went to the side of the bed, meaning to turn the lamp off, but he stopped for a moment, looking down at her. She lay on her back, her head turned slightly toward him. The hollows in her cheeks were very clear, and even in sleep a small frown furrowed her forehead, as though her worries had pursued her into the darkness.

Giles stood for a long time watching her, possessed by feelings that filled him with fear because he couldn't have put them into words. In court he was a skilled orator, but he felt that in her presence he became a clown. If she'd woken and found him there he wouldn't have known what to say. He dreaded it happening, yet the moments passed and still he didn't move.

She sighed and turned her head restlessly. The movement left a strand of fair hair lying across her mouth. He knelt beside her and reached out tentative fingers, trying to brush the strand away without waking her. Now he could see her mouth as he'd never seen it before. He'd known it glossily made-up, laughing, deliberately provocative to make a fool of him. He'd known it tense with anger, hurling cruel and bitter words to shame him. But now it lay in curves as soft and defenseless as a child's. Compassion wrenched him, although he knew she'd reject his compassion as she'd rejected everything else about him. Scarcely knowing what he did, he leaned forward and touched her mouth gently with his own, not daring to breathe lest he disturb her.

For a long, heart-stopping moment, he let his lips lie on hers. The ache in his heart seemed to pervade his whole being as he felt the soft sweetness of her and longed to gather her in his arms. At last, he found the strength to leave her, but as he tensed himself to pull away he felt her stir beneath him, and in another moment her arms had slid around his neck.

Shock held him still. It was followed by fear lest she wake and her eyes harden with accusation. But the lips sighing against his tasted of honey, and the sensation drained the strength from his limbs. For a long time he knelt there, but eventually he forced himself to draw back a little. She whispered something he couldn't catch. Moving slowly, he put his hands behind his neck and took gentle hold of her wrists, drawing them downward and laying her hands on the counterpane. He switched out the light and rose, backing softly away, his eyes fixed on the bed until he reached the door, pulled it open and fled.

Six

It was light when Rae awoke. The curtains were drawn across the window but the room was suffused in a soft glow that suggested daylight outside. What a relief, she thought, that it was Saturday and she didn't have to rush to work.

Her watch said three-thirty. She frowned. Three-thirty on a winter morning should have meant pitch-dark. She jumped out of bed and threw back the curtains. In the distance she could see a faint sun. Although half hidden by mist, it was plainly the deep cerise of sunset. The day was far advanced.

"I must have slept for nearly twenty hours," she thought. "I was only supposed to be having a doze before dinner."

She took a look around the room, seeing things that she'd been too exhausted to notice the night before. It appeared to be a child's room. The predominant colors were pink and white. The wallpaper and curtains depicted characters from television serials, and the white-painted furniture was covered in transfers of flowers and butterflies curiously interspersed with motorbikes..

There was a lifeless feel to the room. No child would have left it so tidy, and little scratches on the wallpaper showed where pictures had been pinned up and later removed. Giles's daughter must have slept here before she'd left with her mother.

Now Rae noticed that the bed was properly made, with clean sheets and even an electric blanket. Did he keep it that way always, or had he telephoned Mrs. Jones to have it ready for her? It would be just like that cool, calculating brain to have planned every move of last night, she thought. She should be annoyed with him, but she couldn't summon up an ounce of annoyance. She'd needed that long sleep, as he'd known she did. She felt well for the first time in weeks.

She thought of him last night, sitting in his car outside the gates of Kinroy & Son, waiting for her with endless patience, the same patience that he'd shown every moment since their first meeting. She'd told herself often that she'd dismissed him finally, but always he'd found a way to stay in her life. And now he'd be harder than ever to dismiss because last night he'd found a way into her dreams.

At the remembrance of that dream, Rae felt a warmth begin inside her and spread slowly until it pervaded her whole being. In sleep, it had seemed to her that Giles came into the room and kissed her, not with passion as before, but gently. The tenderness of that kiss, so unexpected, so unlike the man she knew him to be, had caused a bittersweet sensation, shocking in its intensity, to flood through her. She'd put up her arms, sliding them around his neck to draw him closer, and her heart had opened to him in perfect trust.

She smiled a little now, in mockery of herself, for it was obvious what had happened. In her dream she'd created a new Giles, one who looked like the real man, but who behaved quite differently. The real Giles was a machine, calculating what he owed in reparation and paying it to the last penny, scrupulously, but without feeling. The "dream" Giles had a heart capable of love and tenderness.

Since dreams came from the subconscious, it was clear that hers was trying to warn her against reading too much into his actions. They proceeded from his own strict sense of justice, and nothing else.

She was glad of the warning. When she thought of her own eager response to his kiss, she could only be grateful that it had been hidden in the privacy of a dream and not exposed to his cynical gaze. How her enemy would laugh to know that while she'd slept he'd breached her strongest defenses without even trying.

She found a bathroom next door and took a shower that washed off the last of the night's sleep. Even to her own eyes, her face looked better. She made her way downstairs. Now that she had more opportunity to observe the house, she could see that Giles's ex-wife had a talent for understated luxury. The furnishings and decor were beautiful and in impeccable taste. Nothing jarred. It was the residence of a successful man, married to a woman who'd been destined from birth to be the wife of a successful man.

But to Rae there was something dead about the perfection. It was like the child's room, a place from which life and love had departed, leaving only the shell behind. She wondered how Giles could bear to live there. Still, perhaps he kept it as a showcase.

But as she reached the bottom of the stairs, Rae heard the last thing she'd expected in this place—the sound of children's laughter. She was standing in a large hallway, one end of which led into a passage. At the end of that passage was a door that opened onto a garden. It stood wide open, and through it Rae could make out two youngsters chasing each other across the grass. She went out and stood watching them.

They were about nine or ten, similarly dressed in jeans and thick sweaters. Their bright, rosy faces were uncannily like each other's and like their father's. Rae had no difficulty identifying them as the children in the photograph on Giles's sideboard. They were playing a game of pursuit, dodging each other round the huge pile of bricks that Frank Kinroy had recently delivered prior to starting work on the extension.

The little girl seemed to be the leader. Her face was brilliant with recklessness, in contrast to the boy's more solemn air. As

Rae watched the girl started a perilous climb up the hill of bricks, giggling madly as some of them slipped away beneath her. Not to be outdone, the boy scowled and started after her.

Rae hesitated. They weren't her children, but she didn't feel that those bricks were stable enough to make a safe playground. But at that moment Giles strode past her and toward his children.

"Come on, both of you, down!" he said in a curt voice.

"Oh, *Daddy*!" two voices wailed in protest.

"I said down, before you hurt yourselves."

"But I'm not hurting myself," said the little girl, who was evidently of an argumentative turn of mind. "I'm just standing here. There's no harm in just *standing* here, is there? I mean, anyone can just stand here. I might be standing on the ground , or standing on the stairs, and you wouldn't say I was hurting myself then. So why can't I just *stand* on some bricks?"

"Melanie—"

"I could stand on a table. I could stand on my bed. I could stand on the draining board in the kitchen—"

"Stop arguing and get down!" Giles snapped.

The boy had already scrambled down and was waiting by his father's side while this altercation was going on. Melanie, sensing defeat, scowled and jumped to the ground, ignoring the hand Giles held out to help her. Giles looked tense. The riotously cheerful atmosphere of only a moment ago was dispelled. In their father's presence, the children became more muted. Even Melanie's vibrant personality seemed diminished, although she continued muttering, "I could stand on the floor, I could stand on a chair, I could stand in the bath, I could stand—"

Giles looked as if he'd like to stem this torrent of words but didn't know how. At that moment, he turned and saw Rae watching him and struggling unsuccessfully to control her laughter.

"Hello," he said.

"Hello," she said. "Are these your children?"

"Yes. Melanie, James, this is Miss Bonham, a...a friend of mine."

The youngsters greeted her politely. Melanie said, ''Did you enjoy sleeping in my room? Daddy said we weren't to make a noise and wake you.''

''You didn't wake me,'' said Rae. ''And I think it's a lovely room..''

''Go into the kitchen, both of you,'' said Giles. ''Mrs. Jones has your tea ready.''

The children bounded away. Rae and Giles looked at each other.

''All right, what's so damned funny?'' he demanded.

''You. I never thought to see you defeated in an argument.''

''I wasn't defeated,'' he said at once, nettled. ''I just couldn't get a word in.''

''Well, that's a way of losing an argument, too. An advocate should know that. She's got exactly your manner of worrying away at something like a terrier with a bone, till the other person doesn't know if he's coming or going.''

''Thank you,'' he snapped. ''I know how to take that, I suppose.''

She stared at him blankly. Then she knew what he'd thought she meant.

''No—Giles, honestly—'' impulsively she put a hand on his arm ''—I wasn't being nasty about...that old business. It's just that she's so like you. She's a marvelous child.''

''She's an endlessly naughty one,'' he growled.

He hadn't seemed to notice her hand on his arm. She removed it quietly and went on, ''Children with any spirit usually are. You should be proud of her.''

''I suppose instead of looking out for her safety you'd have had me engage her in legal argument?'' he said crossly.

''It wouldn't have been a bad idea, actually. It would have absorbed her attention, and while she was distracted you could have lifted her down without her even noticing.''

He gave a brief laugh. ''I can never think of things like that. Perhaps that's why—'' He broke off and shrugged. ''Oh well—''

Perhaps that's why your children aren't at ease with you, she thought. They knew he wasn't on their wavelength.

"Did you sleep well?" he enquired politely.

"Perfectly, thank you. I'm sorry to have imposed on you. I can hardly believe that I've slept so long."

"Sooner or later you had to, and don't talk about imposing on me. I meant you to sleep."

"Thank you. But I think I'd better leave now. You've got your children here and—"

'No," he said quickly. "Don't go just yet. You must have something to eat. I expect you're ravenous. Let's go into the kitchen."

He'd taken her arm and was urging her into the house. Rae didn't argue further. It had dawned on her that she really was famished.

Like the rest of the house the kitchen was a work of art. The colors were warm, with red flagstones on the floor, and cream tiles on the walls. The cupboard doors were polished oak with fittings of burnished metal. Copper pots gleamed on the walls. But to Rae all this beauty was unnaturally perfect. It looked as if it had been organized, not by a woman who enjoyed her kitchen, but by a professional designer hoping to be featured in a glossy housekeeping magazine. She began to be curious about Giles's ex-wife.

Melanie and James were already settled at the pine kitchen table tucking into a substantial tea that Mrs. Jones had laid out. They looked up when their father entered, and again Rae had the impression that their spontaneity became more muted. They weren't afraid of him, but he was alien to them. Although absorbed in their food, they looked at Giles frequently as though trying to pick up silent signals that would guide them through a mine field.

James managed the best because he asked his father questions, and Giles answered with almost visible relief. Even this was sticky as he lacked the gift of simplifying his language. He spoke to James in much the same way he'd have addressed a colleague, and several times the boy had to ask the meaning of a long word. But he seemed a naturally serious child who could cope with this kind of conversation, and at least father and son were talking. Melanie was a different matter. It didn't take Rae long to notice that Giles was totally baffled by his daughter's humorous, vital personality.

"I want you both to keep well away from those bricks," he said once. "Not just now but in the future. Any day now, the builders will be arriving and starting to construct the extension. There'll be all sorts of things lying about, and it'll be even more dangerous."

"What sort of things?" she asked, her eyes wide.

He shrugged. "I don't know. The sort of things builders have."

"But what *sort* of things do builders have?"

"How do I know what builders have?" Giles demanded. "I'm not a builder."

"But if you don't know what the things are, how do you know they're dangerous?" said Melanie innocently.

Giles drew in his breath and looked as if he might be on the verge of telling his daughter not to be cheeky, but Rae forestalled him with a smothered burst of laughter.

"You asked for that," she said when she'd controlled herself.

"Did I?"

"You should have seen it coming a mile away. It's exactly what you'd have said." She smiled at Melanie. "You keep at him. Make him give you a proper answer."

"Thank you!" said Giles through gritted teeth.

"Well, go on," she urged him. "Give your daughter a proper answer. Why is builder's clutter dangerous?"

But he'd recovered himself and made a counterattack.

"You tell her," he said cunningly. "You work for the builder. You know what he'll bring."

Melanie immediately fixed Rae with a basilisk stare. Cheerfully, Rae started to explain. "Well, one of the things he'll bring is a concrete mixer, and you must be sure to stay away from that."

"Why?" said Melanie ruthlessly.

"Because if you fall in you'll get covered in concrete," said Rae. "And it'll set hard with you inside it, so you'll be a concrete statue. Your father will have to set you on a plinth in the garden, with a notice saying This Was Melanie. Birds will come and perch on your head, and people will say 'If only she'd listened to her father and not gone too near the concrete mixer.'"

Melanie's eyes gleamed with appreciation, but she wasn't stuck for an answer.

"No, they won't," she said. "They'll say 'Good riddance!' I'll probably be sold for scrap."

"You couldn't be," said Rae at once. "Concrete isn't worth anything as scrap."

"Melanie's not worth anything, anyway," put in James with brotherly frankness. "We'd have to keep her hanging about, and carve our initials on her feet."

"No, you wouldn't," said Melanie at once, "because I'd stamp on your fingers."

"You couldn't. You wouldn't be able to move."

"I could if I wanted to."

"Let's stick to the point," said Rae hastily.

"What is the point?" said Giles. "I got lost back there." He was grinning.

"The point," said Rae firmly, "is that being a concrete statue would be extremely boring."

"Not if there were some garden gnomes," said Melanie, considering this. "We could have conversations."

"You mean you'd talk and they'd listen," said Giles unexpectedly. "Luckily, garden gnomes have big ears. They'd need to."

The children laughed at this, and Rae looked at Giles with appreciation.

"I think I'll be a builder when I grow up," said Melanie thoughtfully. "Then I can play with the concrete mixer."

"That's an excellent idea," said Rae firmly. "The important thing is to have a purpose. But I should leave concrete mixers alone for the moment, if I were you. Save the fun for when you're grown up."

Melanie nodded, apparently feeling that this was a safisfactory argument. Giles was watching Rae closely. She went on talking as naturally as she could, but it was hard to do this while she was so conscious of his eyes on her, with a new look in them, as if he'd only just seen her.

She found that Melanie and James were likeable children with beautiful manners. Ten-year-old James had a solemnity that Rae felt was probably natural to him, and that reminded her uncannily of his father. Melanie, two years younger, had a vivacious personality and a mind like quicksilver. She was never lost for words, and the words were often clever beyond her years. Rae, recalling Giles's brilliant oratory with only a slight pang, was able to see that Melanie had also inherited an aspect of his mind.

Giles, to her pleasure, had relaxed perceptibly. He'd picked up the lead she'd offered and managed to follow it, although he seemed content to leave most of the talking to her, while he sat watching her closely, a half smile on his face. The children, too, were more at ease in her presence, laughing and capping her nonsense with their own.

But then, just when everything seemed to be going well, it was all blown apart.

Somehow the talk had turned to motorbikes, apparently one of Melanie's favorite topics. She was already planning the day when she'd possess her own, which she could picture down to the last detail.

"You've really gone into it, haven't you?" said Rae, impressed. "Where do you get all this knowledge?"

"From Daddy," said James. "He's motorbike crazy, too."

Giles looked up quickly, on the verge of denying it, but he stopped as if someone had struck him. At the same moment, James gave a little gasp and became confused.

"I meant . . . our other daddy . . ." he stammered.

"It's all right, son. It's all right." Giles made a gesture with his hand, indicating that the subject was closed. The boy turned scarlet, evidently feeling snubbed by his father's curt manner. Rae felt a surge of anger against Giles and looked up, half meaning to protest. But she met his eyes, and what she discovered in them shocked her into silence.

She'd never seen such naked misery on any human being's face. This wasn't irritation or displeasure. It was the raw suffering of a father separated from his young, and Rae called herself a blind fool for not seeing till now that Giles adored his children and was devastated at being parted from them.

His pain seemed to be in her own heart, possessing her entirely. Nothing existed but this suffering and the need to ease it by consoling him. She reached out a hand to Giles, but even as she did so the moment was gone. The mask was over his face again. He was smiling, talking in a voice that was almost natural. James was concentrating on his food, but Melanie's eyes, fixed on her father, had a gentle look that was older than her years.

The sound of a car drawing up outside the house was a relief to everyone.

"That'll be your mother," said Giles quickly, and left the kitchen. Rae heard him open the door and greet somebody, and a female voice replying, then his footsteps went up the stairs. The children were finishing their tea and scrambling down.

A woman appeared in the kitchen doorway. She was in her early thirties with a pretty face and that air of total assurance that is worth any amount of looks. She had dark hair and eyes and vivid, mobile features. She was expensively dressed, and despite being seven months pregnant, managed to look elegant.

"Mummy," said Melanie politely, "this is Rae Bonham. She's a friend of Daddy's. She stayed last night."

It was said in total innocence, but Rae was suddenly embarrassed and hurried to correct the implication.

"In fact, I slept in Melanie's room."

Belinda gave a charming ripple of laugher. It was good-natured, but there was no warmth behind it.

"Run along, you two, and get ready," she said to Melanie and James. "I want to be off soon."

The children scampered out, and the two women were alone. Rae was frowning as she tried to recall an echo. Belinda was oddly familiar to her.

"I'm Belinda Martin, by the way," said Giles's ex-wife. "Honestly, you don't owe me any explanations. I gave up my proprietary rights ages ago. Giles does as he likes these days.

Mind you, he always did do as he liked. Oh, I don't mean that there were other women. As far as I know, he was always totally faithful. Infidelity would have offended his notions of strict justice, you see. He believes a bargain's a bargain, and a man must pay his dues to the last penny."

"Good for him," said Rae evenly. She was disliking Belinda more with every second that passed.

"Oh, my dear, I'm not knocking it. It's just that it's not enough. If all you ask for is technical fidelity, then he was the ideal husband. But if you want a man who knows you're there and puts you first, he's a bad choice."

"But didn't you know he was ambitious when you married him?" said Rae.

"Of course I did, and I thought it was marvelous. But I didn't know what his kind of ambition meant. My father's a judge, and I thought Giles would be just like him. I suppose I was a bit stupid when I was twenty. Anyway, I made a thoroughly bad bargain and then found I was stuck with it."

"And you *don't* believe a bargain's a bargain, do you?" said Rae, looking at her steadily.

Again Belinda gave her little ripple of cool laughter.

"Are you quite sure you spent the night in Melanie's room?" she said. "Never mind. As I said, it's none of my business. But I think you should be warned. If you marry Giles, you'll see him for five minutes a day—by appointment only. Mind you, he'll never forget anniversaries. His secretary has instructions to remind him exactly a week in advance. Outside his work he doesn't exist—or if he does, I could never find him."

"But perhaps you would have if you'd really loved him," said Rae.

Belinda looked her up and down appraisingly.

"I hope you haven't got it as badly as you seem to," she said. "Because if you have, God help you!"

"Look, please believe me, you've got hold of the wrong idea," said Rae with sudden urgency. "I'm not in love with Giles—"

She turned sharply at the sound of footsteps in the hall. Giles had come down the stairs while they were talking and was heading for the kitchen. There was nothing in his face to show that he'd heard anything, but she found herself coloring.

"The children are just coming," he said to Belinda.

Rae slipped out past them, thinking that they might wish to talk privately. Melanie and James came tumbling down the stairs clad in scarves and overcoats.

"Goodbye," said James gravely. "It's been so nice meeting you."

Rae took the hand he held out to her, thinking it was rather like talking to a courteous old gentleman. He made her wonder what Giles had been like at the same age.

"Bye," said Melanie. "Will you be coming again?"

"I . . . don't think so," said Rae cautiously.

"Are you ready to go?" came Belinda's brisk voice from the kitchen door. "Right, let's be off. Goodbye, Miss Bonham. It's been really interesting meeting you."

She opened the front door and went ahead to the waiting car. James said goodbye to his father gruffly and went straight out. He was clearly still embarrassed over his earlier slip. Giles leaned down to kiss his daughter, and she looked up as if to give him a peck. But at the last minute, she stood on tiptoe and threw her arms around his neck, almost suffocating him with her embrace. Giles seemed not to move, but Rae's watchful eyes saw his arms tighten around the little girl.

There was an impatient toot on the car horn. Rae silently fumed at Belinda for cutting short this precious moment that meant so much to Giles. Then Melanie had pulled free and scampered down the path. Rae heard the car door slam and the noise from the engine growing fainter.

Giles stood at the front door, not taking his eyes from the car till it had turned the corner of the street. There was something painful in his stillness. After a long time, he turned away. She saw his face then, full of suffering that he didn't know how to hide. Hardly knowing what she was doing, she opened her arms to him, and he went into them.

She held him closely, knowing that her warmth and the feel of her arms about his body was draining the tension out of him and giving him a kind of peace. She was confused to the bottom of her soul. Life had been so much simpler when she could just hate him, but this raw need that had broken through his defenses touched her heart and made her do things she once wouldn't have thought possible. It made her curve a strong hand protectively about his head, pulling him to her and pressing her cheek against his.

After a few moments, they drew apart. In his eyes, she read embarrassment that he'd shown his weakness, and he turned away quickly from her penetrating gaze.

"Mrs. Jones is still around," he muttered as if to explain his awkwardness. "Look, why don't you stay for dinner? She's a good cook and you need a decent meal. That tea wasn't enough."

Outside the house, the raw March weather was rapidly turning to darkness. Suddenly the prospect of staying there in the warmth was inviting.

"Well, you owe me a dinner from last night," she said lightly. "But I'm a good cook, too. Why don't you give Mrs. Jones a night off?"

"All right," he said after a moment's surprise. "I will."

He called Mrs. Jones, who showed Rae the secrets of the kitchen, including the well-stocked freezer, and departed to her own self-contained flat at the back of the house.

Rae spent the next hour very happily. She might consider the kitchen soulless, but it had everything a chef might want and she was a first-rate cook. Giles watched her, helping out with easy tasks. Finally he said, "You really know what you're doing."

"There's no need to sound so surprised," she said in mock indignation.

"No, I mean you're a creative chef. I don't suppose you learned that in your present life." He stopped, suddenly conscious that to say any more would be offensive. He'd been thinking that her previous life probably hadn't contained anything as useful as cooking lessons.

"My mother taught me," said Rae. "To her, it was an art. She started me early. I was only ten when she died, but I'd taken a lot on board by then. Andrew had loved my mother's cooking. He said no one could do it like her—except me. So I cooked for him and went on learning from books."

"Did you call him Andrew to his face?"

"Oh, yes. He preferred it. He said it was friendly, but I think he was just vain." Her voice was full of loving amusement.

"About his age?" said Giles. "But surely...?" Again he pulled himself up short. Andrew Haines hadn't been a young man at his trial, nor had he looked like one. But to say so would be to open the way for her to hurl Andrew's suffering at him. He began to realize that the past made even the simplest conversation with this woman a mine field.

"Let's have a drink," he said. "You like dry sherry, don't you?"

"Very good," she said admiringly. "Yes, please."

He returned with the bottle and two crystal glasses. As he poured, she said, "You were thinking just now that Andrew looked his age, weren't you? Of course he did. He was in his late fifties. But there's no knowing which direction a man's vanity will take." And the dangerous moment had been defused.

"I'm afraid your ex-wife has got the wrong idea about us," she said. "Melanie introduced me as 'Daddy's friend who stayed all night.'"

He grinned. "Trust my little girl to land me right in it." Then a cloud came over his face and he said, "I'm glad you got on with them so well. You were on their wavelength right from the start. I wish you'd tell me how you do it. There's something I just can't—" He shrugged helplessly. "I want to talk to them, but I'm like a man trying to tune an elusive radio station in boxing gloves. If I talk normally, it goes above their heads because my talk is geared to adults. If I try to talk down to them, I overdo it and sound like an idiot. They think so, too, I can tell. I see them looking at me and thinking 'Who does he imagine he's fooling?' But you tuned in right away."

"But I didn't talk down to them," she said. "To reach a child's level you don't go down, you go sideways, to a different place."

"But where is it? How do I find it?" he said. He spoke lightly, but she could clearly hear the undertone of desperation.

"I don't know how to tell you," she said, frowning. "It's easy for me, because in many ways my father stayed a child all his life. He and I were close from the very first moment. Perhaps that's the real reason I call him Andrew. It felt natural because in a sense we were always on the same level.

"I had a wonderful childhood. Maybe that's why I've survived these past few years so well. If you're happy as a child it gives you something you never lose again. It wasn't anything to do with money. Oh, Andrew bought me expensive presents, yes. He loved giving things, but all those gifts were chosen with enormous care. He didn't send his secretary out for them. He went to the toy stores himself, and he always got the right toys, because he understood me. He spent time with me, you see."

Rae didn't know that her memories had brought a soft flush to her cheeks and a light to her eyes that the man watching her had never seen before. He held his breath, not daring to move or speak lest he break the spell.

"Shall I tell you about the most wonderful gift he ever gave me?" she went on. "I was eleven years old. Andrew came into the room and found me doing some embroidery. He sat down beside me and asked me about it. I explained everything in great detail, going over every stitch and every color. He stayed with me for an hour, asking me questions and telling me how clever I was. I was on top of the world. I thought I must be the most interesting person who'd ever lived.

"Much later I found out that Andrew had been involved in a terribly complicated crisis at the time. Someone had been trying to take him over and he was fighting off enemies on several fronts. But he found time to spend that hour with me. It was always like that. If we were talking, he'd give me all his attention. If I visited him at his office, he'd tell his secretary to hold all phone calls, no matter who. I always knew I was the center of his life. He gave me self-confidence, and that's the greatest gift of all.

"You've sometimes said to me that I ought to face the truth about my father, meaning that he was a crook. I know he was. But truth isn't simple and straightforward. It has so many different sides. Andrew was a *wonderful* father. That was the truth about him, too."

Giles's face was drawn. "I suppose I have to face the fact that my children would never say that about me," he said. "They've almost forgotten that I'm their father at all."

"No, they haven't," she said. "That slip of the tongue didn't really mean anything. It's not what children call you that matters, but how they think of you. You must let them know how much you love them and miss them, particularly James. Melanie knows. That's why she gave you that extra hug before she went. She was trying to tell you that she loves you, too."

The eagerness in Giles's face was painful to behold. "Do you really believe that, Rae? You're not just saying it to comfort me?"

"I know it's true. Didn't you feel it when she put her arms round you?"

"I thought I did," said Giles hesitantly.

Never before had she seen this strong, confident man so unsure of himself. He seemed scared to believe in what he most wanted, as though he couldn't face the pain of disillusionment, and this awareness of his fear confused Rae still more. It was totally unlike the Giles Blake that she thought she knew. But she was beginning to understand that the truth about this man was also many sided, and that perhaps she didn't know him at all.

Seven

They ate at one end of a large rosewood table in the dining room. Giles had made an efficient job of laying out the cutlery and glasses.

"Now it's my turn to be surprised," said Rae as they began to eat. "Somehow I never pictured you as handy about the house."

"I'm certainly not a househusband," said Giles so hastily that she chuckled. "But I grew up knowing how to make myself useful. I had to. I did my share of the chores or I got the back of my mother's hand. I was glad of it later on when she was ill and I had to look after her and run the house."

"What about your father?" said Rae, intrigued by this new glimpse of Giles.

"I never saw my father after I was ten, thank God," he said so fervently that she stared. "He's probably alive somewhere. I'd like to meet him, just once, so that I could have the pleasure of smashing his front teeth in for all the times he did it to my mother. But apart from that, I couldn't care less whether he's alive or dead." He saw her expression and grinned. "Now I've shocked you."

"No, it's just that this seems so unlike you."

"And what is like me?" he said seriously. "Do you know?"

"No, I suppose I don't," she confessed. "I thought I did, but I was just looking at one side, wasn't I?"

He nodded. "And that's not even the 'real' side—if there is a real side, which I often doubt. I set out years ago to make myself over into another man. Now I've forgotten what the original one was like, except that he could only think of one thing—getting away from his background."

"That was the slum you were telling me about?" she said. "I wish you'd tell me more, Giles. I'd like to understand."

He frowned, and she knew she'd asked something very difficult for him. He liked to keep the conversation external, with attention focused on others. He flinched when it came too close to himself. Now she was asking him to reveal secrets he'd hidden so long ago that he'd forgotten where he'd put them.

"I don't know that I understand anything myself," he said at last. "I've never tried to sort out the memories of my childhood, because that would mean thinking about them. They're just there like a dark shadow always in the background, always menacing me. When I was young I was driven by the dread of being trapped in poverty and hopelessness forever. I thought when I passed my exams and got a good job the fear would go. But it was only replaced by the terror of being sucked back. So I drove myself harder still, to put more distance between the past and me. It doesn't work, though. There isn't enough money or success in the world to stop the past from haunting me.

"I remember my father as a violent, drunken bully. He was a big, stupid man who used his fists to win every argument. He was out of work more often than he was in it, and when he worked, he drank most of what he earned. That was why we lived in slums. They were all we could afford. Sometimes we had only one room. The electricity was constantly being disconnected because there was no money to pay the bills. When my mother managed to get Social Security payments, he drank them away. If she protested, he hit her.

"My mother never yielded an inch. She wouldn't let him see she was scared of him. She had a sharp tongue and she could tie him in knots. So he'd hit her again to shut her up, but she wouldn't stop. That would have been giving in, you see, and to my mother the worst sin you could commit was to give in. She lived for just one thing—to see me get out. Everything was subordinated to that.

"My father wanted me to be like himself, and it didn't take him long to see that I was going my mother's way. He hated it that I was good at school. He thought books were namby-pamby. A real man, in his eyes, did manual work—when he did any at all. In his spare time he'd drink, smoke and knock his wife around. That was the manly ideal. My God, if you knew how I came to hate his stupid, ignorant yap about what 'a man' was supposed to be!" He broke off suddenly and poured himself another drink.

Rae pushed her chair back, glad that the serving of the next course gave her the excuse to escape for a breather. Giles's memories were proving more harrowing than she'd expected. His air of tension was sharper than ever, but now he'd started, he seemed determined to drive himself to the limit. She'd go the distance with him, but the pictures that were flooding her mind filled her with a horror that needed momentary relief.

When they were halfway through the main course, she said, "What happened when your father saw you were pulling away from him? Did he start knocking you around, too?"

He sat down his fork and stared at her.

"Is it that obvious?" he said at last.

"It was a reasonable guess."

"He'd always been inclined to thump me at odd moments, but not very much because right from the start he saw me as 'a buddy' for him. He was just waiting for me to grow old enough. When he realized I was taking my mother's side, it all became different. To him it was virtually a betrayal, and I'm sure he started to hate me. After that—well, let's say that I've never laid a hand on my own children.

"It was one of the things Belinda and I used to quarrel over. She thought I was totally irrational, and in a way she's right. But I've always been adamant about it—" Giles smiled wryly "—even when Melanie's kitten relieved himself all over some important papers I was due to take into court the next morning, after I'd told her a thousand times to keep him out of my study. I ground my teeth over that a bit, but I didn't smack her and I wouldn't let Belinda. I remember too much, you see. I couldn't even begin to hurt them, or risk their loathing me as I loathed my father."

She felt as though the earth had shaken beneath her. She'd have taken her oath that Giles Blake was a man of stony hardness, ruthless to the world and probably a martinet to his children. To discover instead this raw, painful sensitivity, this aching need to be loved, made her feel that nothing was as it seemed anymore. Black was white, up was down, inside was out, and Rae Bonham, who'd never questioned her own self-righteous judgment, was a fool.

"But you got rid of him at last, when you were ten?" she said.

"Yes, he walked out. I think he found himself another woman, but I'm not sure. My mother didn't pretend to mourn him. In fact, she uprooted and we went to live in a different area so that if he came back he couldn't find us. For years afterward we both flinched whenever we heard a step outside, in case it was him.

"It was my mother's obsession that I should do well. She took cleaning jobs to support us, but to make enough to live on, she had to work all hours. That was when I became a proficient housekeeper. I'd get home from school and have the tea ready when she came in. She'd dash home, have a quick bite to eat, then go off out again cleaning offices. I'd spend the evening doing my homework, and at ten o'clock I'd clear away and pour the milk into the saucepan, ready for the cocoa. I'd put it on the gas as soon as I heard her key in the lock.

"We'd drink our cocoa together and she'd ask me about my homework. It was practically an interrogation. She nailed every detail down, she was so determined I was going to get on. 'Get on and get out,' she used to say. At other times she said, 'You're going to escape. I've set my heart on that.'

"Then she'd send me to bed while she stayed up to do the housework. Often I'd creep down in the early hours and find her asleep in the chair. She'd worked till she couldn't keep her eyes open anymore. I'd beg her to get some more rest, but she couldn't seem to stop. She was driven by demons.

"Once I skimped on my homework and did the clearing up myself. I couldn't wait for her to come in and see what I'd done. I pictured her face, how pleased she'd be—" Giles gave a wry half smile in mockery of himself.

"And wasn't she?" said Rae gently.

"Far from it. I'd never seen her so angry. She called me a fool for putting something before my work. I tried to tell her that I wanted her to get some rest, but she said the only rest she'd ever know was to see me escape." Giles's eyes darkened with remembered pain. "I couldn't make her understand. It's strange now, after all these years—"

"I know," she said quickly. "Some things go on hurting as though they'd happened yesterday." She was filled with rage at the woman who'd hurt the little boy by her apparent rejection of his loving gesture.

"Didn't she understand that you did it because you loved her?" she said in a soft voice.

Giles shook his head. "I don't suppose I explained it very well. I've never known the words for that sort of thing. My mother wasn't—" he shrugged "—she wasn't a demonstrative person. She loved me. I was her whole life but...she didn't like being kissed or touched, even by me. She said it was 'soppy.' She proved her love by working herself to the bone for my sake. She said that was real love, not 'acting silly.'"

This time Rae could find no words for the feelings that possessed her. She thought of the child, brutalized by one parent and rejected by the other, struggling to find an outlet for his affection. He'd been denied tenderness and warmth by the very person who loved him most. The wonder wasn't that he found these things hard to express now, but that there was any left in him, at all. Whatever was gentle and loving in Giles's character came from neither parent. It was all his own, the result of his fumbling attempts to find something in the world that was neither cruel nor cold. She thought of the terrible, frustrated love she'd seen on his face as she'd said goodbye to his children, and wondered what sort of man nature had meant him to be.

She began to argue illogically, as though her arguments could reach back and convince the woman who'd been Giles's mother.

"But I thought she said you had to help in the house," she said.

"Specific jobs, yes, where it couldn't be avoided. But nothing extra. Time belonged to schoolwork. Nothing mattered but getting ahead. Luckily, I was good at school, although never quite good enough for her. Whatever marks I got, she wanted to know why they hadn't been higher."

"But that's dreadful," said Rae indignantly, "driving you like that—"

"No, it's not dreadful," said Giles. "Of course it's not how we're supposed to educate children now, is it? These days you're supposed to be 'enlightened' and not ask your children to do anything they don't want to. I'll admit that I've never driven my two the way my mother drove me. But if she hadn't made me slave every minute, I might not have made it out of the slums. So I'm not complaining. It's just that—"

He broke off and shrugged in a way Rae was becoming used to. It was his invariable gesture when trying to express a thought he found hard to put into words. But with that knowledge of his deepest heart that seemed to be growing in her every minute, she found that she could finish the thought for him. If his mother had been able to express her love in hugs and kisses, the lonely child might have grown up into a man who was happy as well as successful, at ease in the presence of love instead of confused by it.

Behind Giles's forbidding exterior there was a deep vein of raw feeling that no one had ever tapped, because the one woman who might have made it flower early had taught him to be ashamed of it. His father, for all his brutality, had harmed

Giles less than the mother who'd rejected the best in him in favor of a soulless ambition.

No wonder, she thought, that the cool, unsympathetic Belinda hadn't been able to cope with him. She wouldn't have begun to know how to help this difficult man. Giles needed a woman whose own emotional security was like a rock, so that she could accept him at his worst without ever ceasing to love him. He needed, in fact, a woman like Rae herself, whose happy childhood had given her a security that nothing could shake, although until tonight she hadn't fully understood that.

She stopped herself there, amazed at the turn her thoughts had taken. But still the echo of an idea lingered.... Under different circumstances she could have loved Giles and taught him to love, as no other woman could do.

"Tell me," she said gently, "if you didn't do as well as she expected, what happened?"

"If you mean did she hit me, no. In a sense nothing 'happened.' But the atmosphere froze, and I always knew that she was disappointed in me."

"So you'd work harder than ever to unfreeze the atmosphere?"

"You must be gifted with second sight tonight," he said. "That's exactly what I used to do. I was so scared."

"Did she ever say she was pleased with you? What about when you passed your final exams? You must have passed them really well."

"I did, but she never knew. She was dying at that time. She was just worn out with all those years. She'd had one heart attack, and we knew the next would be the last. But she hung on grimly. She was determined to hear my results." His mouth twisted. "She missed them by one day."

And he'd missed her longed-for approval by one day. He didn't say it, but he didn't need to. When he looked up and met her eyes Rae saw that he knew she'd understood the unspoken thought.

Suddenly she was afraid. The old danger signals that had always flashed on in Giles's presence had failed her tonight. Disarmed and foolishly confident, she'd strayed into dangerous territory. Now the signals were flashing again, warning her to get out while there was still time.

"I'd better clear away and get us some coffee," she said abruptly.

She told herself that it was only sensible to get through the meal quickly. It was dark and cold outside, and she still had the journey home ahead of her. But she knew she was a coward.

Giles had brought some of the dishes from the table and stacked them in the sink. Now he stood in the kitchen door watching her make the coffee.

"You don't have to go," he said. "You can sleep in Melanie's room again. I won't disturb you."

"I'd better go home," she said, busily not looking at him. "I really must."

"All right," he said in a toneless voice after a moment. "I'll drive you home later. We'll have our coffee in the next room."

The dining room led through an arch into a small sitting room, where a low table stood near a fire. Rae exclaimed when she saw it.

"A real open fire! I thought they didn't exist anymore."

"This one wouldn't exist if Belinda had had her way. When we bought this house, it needed a lot of work. She did it all from scratch, including tearing out the fireplaces and putting in central heating. But I managed to save this one. She thought it was the grossest sentimentality."

"Well, if you're sentimental, so am I," said Rae, setting out the cups. "But I guess she isn't."

The tart edge to her voice caught his attention.

"You didn't like her, did you?" he said.

"Not a bit."

"Why?"

"Oh, all sorts of things," she said uncomfortably. She couldn't tell Giles the real reason his ex-wife had caused her hackles to rise. That would mean facing it herself.

"Were you very much in love with her?" Rae had meant not to ask the question, but it came out, anyway.

"I thought I was. Maybe I talked myself into it, I don't know. The fact is—" he colored slightly "—this is going to sound conceited, but she seemed to make a bee-line for me. I couldn't understand it. I was young, poor, struggling to survive on what I earned from the odd case, and my company manners weren't exactly polished. I was so scared of doing or saying the wrong thing that I grunted at everyone. The words came easily in court, but out of it I was virtually inarticulate. Yet she seemed to like me. I was flattered, knocked for a loop."

"She liked you," said Rae tartly, "because she could see you were going to end up a judge—just like Daddy."

"I discovered that eventually. At the time I was so preoccupied with keeping my head above water that it never occurred to me that anyone saw me as a potential judge.

"Of course everyone thought I'd married her with an eye to the main chance, but funnily enough, it wasn't that. I thought marrying her would be like coming in out of the cold. We'd have children. That was the only difference her money made in my eyes. It meant we could afford to start our family at once, and I wanted that.

"At first, everything was fine. We bought a small run-down house, and she started work transforming it. I thought it showed what a natural homemaker she was. But when it was finished and looking marvelous, she wanted to move out and start again somewhere else. She just loved doing up old houses. This one was our third. When we divorced, I offered to be the one to move out, but she refused. Her present husband lives in a ramshackle barn, apparently. She couldn't wait to get started.

"I never really knew what Belinda wanted from me. Initially, she was as ambitious as I was. Unluckily for me, she knew too much. She'd been raised among top advocates, she'd seen them at work and she regarded success as natural. I had my early failures, some of them caused by sheer stupidity on my part. And it didn't go down well that I always knew she was thinking what so-and-so would have done. I felt I was competing with an unseen crowd of the best men. If I failed, I felt I was letting her down.

"I put everything I had into not failing, perhaps too much. But it meant long hours shut up alone poring over papers. Her father had been a judge for most of her life, so all she'd seen was life at the top. The reality of a beginner trying to make his name was a nasty shock to her. Anyway, her heart went out of it in the end. I can't honestly say I blame her for finding someone else.

"If I'd been a different kind of man I might have made it easier on her, convinced her that I loved her even if I lived with my work most of the time. But that would have taken subtlety, which I'm not good at." Giles gave a wry smile of mockery, directed at himself. "Not with people, anyway. I'm all right with evidence. In fact, that's really the only thing I'm good at. Once I thought it would be enough."

In the firelight Rae could see his face was haggard and drawn. She crouched by the low table where she'd put the coffee things and refilled his cup. But then, instead of going back to her seat, she sat on the floor where she was and started to poke the fire. She did this without any calculation at what might happen afterward. She simply wanted to be nearer to him.

"Belinda had a familiar look," she said, concentrating on the fire. "I'm sure I've seen her somewhere before."

"You did," said Giles, "but I'm surprised you remember. It was eight years ago. She was in court for the trial, sitting just in front of you in the public gallery."

The picture of a very pretty young woman who'd turned and regarded her with supercilious amazement as she'd screamed her accusation to Giles came into Rae's mind.

"Yes, now I remember," she said. "She looked heavily pregnant."

"That was Melanie. She was born six weeks later. I told myself I was on top of the world. Work poured in after your father's case. I had two lovely children, everything a man could want."

She turned away from the fire and rested her arms on the table, looking up at him.

"So what was wrong?" she said.

"You. I couldn't get rid of you. You were there in my mind calling me a smug, self-satisfied bastard." As if in a dream he began to recite, "'You don't care what happens to anyone as long as you make your lousy money. You'll destroy us and forget us, because people are nothing to you. But I won't forget you. One day I'll come back and make you wish you hadn't done it.' "

She stared at him. "Did I say all that? I know I said I'd come back, but the rest—I hardly remember the exact words myself."

"But I remember them, every one. You were wrong about one thing. I didn't forget you. You've haunted me, Tanis Haines. You've been a shadow that's touched everything in my life, making it a mockery. It was a long time before I could admit to myself the real reason you troubled me. It was because you made me see the truth about what I was becoming.

"I'm a lawyer, you see. I talk a lot about truth, but at heart I don't really like the word. No lawyer does, because we all know we play games with it.

"It's such an unreal world in court. People go into the witness box and swear to tell 'the truth, the whole truth, and nothing but the truth,' but they never do tell the truth, because none of them know it. All they can tell are the facts, and even the facts are incomplete.

"Sometimes the truth seems so simple. You know a man is a crook, and all you've got to do is prove it. So you hammer away at the facts that show his guilt, and it's all neat and tidy. But then sometimes you come across him again in the outside world, where things are more complex than they ever are in court. And you find that nothing is as you thought, and what you've 'proved' is only a partial truth. I don't mean that he's innocent. I don't think I've ever caused an innocent man to be found guilty. But his guilt isn't the only facet of him. In the final analysis, it may not even be the one that matters."

He looked away from her as he said the next words. "But you confront other people in court, as well, innocent people who've become caught up—" A shudder seemed to possess him. "Rae, for God's sake! I was young and hungry for success. . . ." He dropped his head into his hands.

At once she rose to her knees and reached up to him. He raised his head to look at her, and she took his face in her hands. For a long moment they didn't move. He searched her face, frowning as if afraid of what he'd find there. But when she drew him toward her and kissed him on the mouth, his arms went around her as if seeking home.

She began the kiss gently, offering him warmth and comfort. She wanted only to drive the torment from his eyes. But the feel of his mouth against hers was bittersweet, and she lingered to savor the sensation of warm, firm lips that savored hers in return.

Giles had sensed the change in her, the moment when reassurance became shock and then temptation. He knew there was more than kindness in the enticing movements of her lips, but to discover what else there might be meant following the enticement to the end. The imperative need to do so drove out the last of his caution.

The sudden urgency in his clasp was a warning to Rae. Pull away now, cried the voice of sanity in her mind. Pull back while there's time to pretend you were only being friendly. But it was already too late to pull back. The blood sang in her veins, and his arms held her firmly as though he'd divined her thoughts and was determined to keep her there.

But she wasn't going anywhere. She was under a spell, and Giles was the magician who knew just how to caress her mouth with his own till she swayed like someone in a hypnotic trance. Then his tongue joined in the enchantment, tracing the outline of her lips until they fell apart, gasping, and he could take possession.

The slow exploration of his tongue filled her with fear because it told her of her own need. It had been there from the start, waiting to leap into flames at the right moment. But foolishly she'd thought she'd brought it under control. Now she discovered that she wanted to taste him, devour him, melt into him, feel him melt into her. She longed to experience his body, to see it, feel it beneath her hands, between her thighs, to be crushed by its weight and have the scent of his dark maleness in her nostrils.

Tonight she'd felt in danger because his loneliness had touched her heart. But what shook her now had nothing to do with that mild feeling. This was a raw, lustful urgency, as shocking as it was exhilarating.

She began to tease him, challenging his tongue with her own, with her lips and teeth.

"For God's sake, Rae," he growled.

His hands had begun to explore her slim body, setting off trails of fire through the material. At last, he found the buttons of her shirt and began to work on them with fingers that shook.

"I want to see you," he whispered. "I've always wanted that, ever since the first night. That dress suggested everything and gave away nothing. Now I have to know the truth about you."

"What is truth?" she teased him. "You hate the word. It's something to play games with."

"Do you think you can get away with playing games with me?" he growled. "We'll have a moment of truth tonight, you little witch."

"Hussy," she reminded him. "You said I was a hussy."

"*You* told *me* you were a hussy, and you were right. *Do you know what you're doing to me?*"

"Show me," she whispered against his mouth.

He found with pleasure that his ability to concentrate on two things at once was valuable even in this situation. For while he'd been talking, his fingers had continued their work uninterrupted, and now her shirt was open to the waist. But beneath it there was the even more tantalizing covering of a soft, lace-edged slip, and beneath that an invitingly flimsy bra.

He felt for the fastening of her skirt and began to negotiate the button. At once she pulled back from him, keeping her hands on his shoulders so that she drew him with her down to the floor. The movement was fluid like the swirling of water. She had the softness and fluidity of water, too, he discovered, for all at once her hands dropped away from him and she lay there, motionless except for the rapid rise and fall of her breasts.

If Giles had found it easy to think in images, or if he'd ever been at sea, he'd have known that water is never so dangerous as when it lies unusually still, its tranquillity masking the turbulence beneath. He saw only Rae's calm surface, her wide eyes, bright with desire, and softly parted lips. He couldn't know that deep inside her, in her loins, a submerged whirlpool of excitement was spinning faster and faster. The feel of his urgently moving fingers through her clothes drove her half mad with anticipation. But she refused to hurry him.

He'd freed the waistband of her skirt. She moved to let him ease it down over her hips. His hands went swiftly upward on her long legs, the fingertips sliding beneath her slip. He'd meant only to take hold of it to pull it up and over her head, but the feel of her thighs distracted him. His hands lingered, caressed, moved on toward the tops, allowing his palms to cup the soft fullness of her bottom and pause there a moment, while he savored the sudden delight.

Looking up into his face, Rae saw it suffused with a desire that matched her own. It had the same naked, unguarded look she'd seen once before, when they'd danced the first night.

Other memories of that night came flooding back—how she'd watched him during the speeches, wondering if this man would be as formal and correct as a lover as he was as a lawyer. She partly guessed the answer now she'd discovered some of his heart, but the truth about that big, strong body was still hidden from her. He'd promised her a moment of truth....

She saw the shock on his face as she reached up and began to undress him. Then he took his hands from her and drew away sharply. While Rae was still wondering what he meant to do, he reached over and switched off the lamp that was the room's sole artificial light. Now there was only the glow from the fire to illuminate them.

At once he was beside her on the carpet again, ripping buttons open himself, until she sensed, rather than saw, that he was naked. The fire had fallen low and she could make out only an outline of an arm, a muscular torso, a length of thigh. She longed to put the light back on and see if his body was as magnificent as her senses were telling her it was. But he was pulling her slip over her head, feeling his way to the fastening of her bra, then the waistband of her tights, which vanished as if by magic. Her panties followed abruptly and were tossed away into the darkness.

A rasping sensation against her palms told her that his chest was covered with thick, curly hair. She began to explore, seeking to find its limits. As her hands slid lower, the texture of the hair began to change. It became finer, softer, so that her fingers slid easily across the flat stomach to the place where the hair narrowed down, and suddenly her hands were full of him, hard and warm and powerful, the taut urgency throbbing against her palms.

She was on her back on the carpet again, the heavy presence looming over her. A hand parted her legs, fingers gently touching the inner thighs that were aching for him. Her toes curled in unbearable anticipation as the fingers moved slowly, encountering the moist warmth that was his welcome.

At once he moved over her. Her legs seemed to curve of their own accord to encompass him. She let out a long, moaning sigh as he took what she offered, claiming her deeply with long, slow thrusts that drove her wild.

"Rae . . ." he whispered hoarsely, then again, *"Rae . . ."* in a voice that was half a groan. He said her name over and over, as though just the sound of it had some magic symbolism that would link him forever to this ecstatic momemt. She tried to murmur his name, but found that there was no name for the seering sweetness that filled her with every thrust. It simply existed, possessing her utterly, so that she ceased to be herself and become him, as he was her.

He was moving slowly inside her, savoring his possession with wonder. Above her, Rae could see his eyes shining in the darkness, but the rest of his face was hidden. How was he looking at her? she wondered wildly. With lust, with satisfaction, or perhaps with the same tenderness she'd known from him once before, in a kiss that had been part of a dream . . . ?

But this was nothing but a dream, this devastating sensation of his hard maleness inside her, making her body his own, this piercing, beautiful desire with which he was driving her to madness; it was all a dream that must never be allowed to end. Her arms were strong and determined around him, her hands tense against the hard muscles of his back, drawing him fiercely closer.

"Again," she whispered, "again—again—oh, Giles—"

The whirlpool within her was gathering speed. She cried out her release as she went spinning into its depths, plunging endlessly to the place where the dream ended.

Giles lay with his head pillowed on her breasts. He was totally still. He felt as if he'd been caught in an earthquake, and now that it was over nothing in a once familiar landscape would ever be the same. He became slowly aware that her hands were clasped behind his head in a gesture that seemed to him to be an acceptance of himself and everything that had just happened.

Rae was also motionless beneath him, except that her breasts rose and fell slowly as her breathing grew calmer. She hadn't moved since their mutual release. Her legs were around him and their bodies were still in intimate contact.

He pulled back a little. By the fire's soft glow he could just make out her pale shape beneath him. Her breasts were more generous than clothes made them appear, and he ran his fingers gently over them, wondering at their ripe beauty.

His eyes drifted to her face, and what he saw there made him stop. She had the same vulnerable, defenseless look he'd seen once before, and swiftly he pulled her upright and into his arms, cradling her against his chest as if trying to comfort her, although he couldn't have said why.

But even now his hands couldn't resist the temptation to wander over her, relishing details of her lovely body that the urgency of his passion had made him overlook before. He discovered soft, gentle curves that filled him with delight as he caressed her.

Then he became aware that she was engaged in a similar occupation. Her hands had found their way around him and had begun an exploration of their own, tracing the lines of his shoulders, his lean hips, his firm, muscular buttocks, the long line of his flanks. She, too, lingered, making lazy circling movements as though his body had been made exclusively for her pleasure.

He stiffened and felt a shock go through him, for his upbringing had turned him into a conventional man, and nothing in his marriage had taught him to be otherwise. But the purposeful movements of her fingers were evoking sensations that were stronger than inhibition, and gradually he relaxed in her arms.

When she turned her face up to him, he bent and kissed it. Still with his mouth on hers, he rose to his feet, drawing her with him. Absorbed in the kiss, Rae didn't realize what was happening until she felt herself lifted in his arms. Another moment and his movements told her that they were climbing the stairs. She buried her face against him, wanting to shut out details and be aware only of him.

She felt the softness of a sheet beneath her back and opened her eyes. She was in a bedroom, but not the one in which she'd slept the previous night. Two long windows with the curtains drawn back let in a pale glow from the moon, but there was no other light. Then she forgot her surroundings again in the overwhelming awareness of Giles.

He'd resumed his exploration, taking time to relish the silky texture of her skin with his fingertips, then with his lips and tongue. Her breath caught in her throat as her body reawakened to his caresses and heat began to surge through her once more. His mouth had claimed one proudly peaked nipple and was teasing it as though he had all the time in the world. At each flicker of his tongue, stabs of excitement possessed her, mounting in intensity.

How could this happen, she thought wildly, so soon after their previous loving? What black magic was he master of that he could command her body to respond to him with the same urgency as before, and it had no choice but to obey?

But if she belonged to him, he also belonged to her, and she reached out for what was hers, with hands that demanded while they caressed. She arched against him and felt him aroused and strong against her. She parted her legs and would have drawn him inside but he paused, fearing her power, wanting to control their union.

For a long moment, a silent, sensual battle raged between them, but the outcome was never in real doubt. With a groan he yielded and sought the warm, sweet place that welcomed him, feeling the embrace of her silky thighs, knowing he was lost.

He took her powerfully as though, having revealed his weakness, he must show her that she, too, was helpless in the grip of desire. Blissfully she let him have his way. This was one victory she had no wish to deny him. She'd had her own and it had given her everything she wanted. The muscles of his back and flanks were made of steel. She felt them tense again and again as he claimed her with vigorous movements, and a long, low moan of ecstasy broke from her. The moment of her fulfilment was an explosion of darkness within her.

When it was over, she lay still, exhausted and drained, with hardly the strength even to move. But she just managed to raise a hand and slide it around his neck. His arms were beneath her, lifting her, cradling her against him. Then she realized she was asleep because the dream had returned, sweeter and more tender than before. It was the last thing she knew.

Eight

When Rae awoke next morning, she couldn't remember where she was. She was lying alone in a large bed in an unfamiliar room. She pulled herself up and saw that she was wearing nothing. Then memory came back to her in a torrent. She looked down at that naked body and the thought of how it had behaved the night before sent a wave of heat through her. Those long limbs had twined possessively around him; those loins had thrust against him again and again, demanding him deeper and deeper inside her.

She could hardly bear to think of it, so great was her horror at her betrayal of her father. She'd allowed herself to forget that Giles was the man who'd persecuted Andrew for his own ends. He'd as good as admitted it the night before, and within an hour of his admission she'd gone to his bed. She groaned and buried her face in the pillow, swamped by anguish.

Abruptly she sat up and flung herself out of bed. Nothing mattered now but to get away from here as soon as possible.

The bedroom had its own bathroom. In a moment she was under the shower, making the water first cold, then hot, trying to wash away the memories that were imprinted in her flesh. She twisted this way and that under the water, seeking absolution, but it was useless. There was no part of her that he hadn't touched the night before, with his lips, his hands or his loins, no part of her that she hadn't offered to him in shameless abandon. Her body belonged to him because he had raised in it such a storm of desire that all other loyalties were silenced. It was his, and he had only to touch it to claim it. That was something that couldn't be washed off by soap and water.

But it could be hidden. Never, by word or deed, would she allow him to guess the full extent of his victory over her. Bitterness rose in her as she thought of Andrew and the way she'd betrayed him. She hated Giles for being the cause of that betrayal. She clutched the side of the shower, weak with the force of her feelings, but letting them possess her, because they'd give her the strength to say what she must. She wanted to rend him apart with her hatred, because then she might hate herself a little less.

She switched off the water and stepped out. When she was dry she wrapped a large, clean bath towel around herself and opened the bathroom door. Then she stopped on the threshold, held silent by what she saw.

Giles had come into the bedroom with a tray on which stood a teapot, a cup and a milk jug. He'd placed it on a low table beside the bed and was standing over it, plainly dissatisfied. As Rae watched, he rearranged the cup and jug, then the jug and teapot. Finally he put everything back in its original place. When he moved the cup, it rattled slightly in the saucer as though his hand wasn't quite steady. Every line of his body betrayed his tension.

Rae was hardly aware that she'd let out her breath in a long sigh, but he heard it and looked up quickly. As he came toward her she saw his eyes, and the cruel words died on her lips.

He was nervous. He smiled but the apprehension was there in his eyes as he searched her face, and suddenly she remembered what a rejection meant to him. Last night he'd confided to her things she guessed he'd never revealed to another soul. She thought of the words she'd meant to hurl at him and knew she'd come close to destroying a man without defenses. She was almost faint with relief that she'd stopped in time.

"Hello," he said. "I brought you tea."

"Lovely. I'm dying for a cup." She had no idea what she was saying.

"Come and sit down. I'll pour it for you."

"Do you have another dressing gown I could borrow?" she said. She was intensely aware that the towel covering her was none too secure. Giles was in pajamas with a brown silk dressing gown over them.

"Sure," he said at once and went to his wardrobe, taking out a robe of red silk. She managed to put it on while still wearing the towel, then to let the towel slide out from below. As she tied the belt firmly, she wasn't certain that she'd made a good exchange. The thin silk provided only a flimsy covering for her body. She felt sure he could look through it and see how her flesh was tingling with the consciousness of what they'd shared. But then she knew he wouldn't need to look. His own flesh must also be alive with memory, as perfectly in tune with her own as when they'd lain together in the white heat of passion. The echo of that passion would endure as long as life itself.

She drank her tea, conscious that he was watching her, although she wouldn't look at him.

"Rae," he said at last, "we have to talk."

She gave a self-conscious laugh. "Didn't we talk enough last night?"

"Last night was only a beginning."

She put her cup down suddenly and passed a hand over her eyes.

"No, it has to be an end, Giles. It shouldn't have happened."

"How can you say that?" he demanded, frowning. "It was bound to happen."

He was right, she knew. From the moment she'd walked across the room toward him on that very first evening and they'd looked at each other and felt the current that flowed between them, it had been inevitable. Everything else had been merely the prelude to the consummation of a passion too overwhelming to be denied.

But passion was not all that lay between them. They were connected by cruel, bitter memories that still lived, poisoning what might have been beautiful. Last night she'd sampled forbidden fruit, and the memory would sear her as long as she lived. The longing might never die, but the fruit would remain forbidden, and now she must turn away with the taste of it still sweet on her lips.

"Maybe it was bound to happen once," she said. "But it can never happen again. You know why."

"I'm damned if I know why. When we talked last night, I thought you understood—"

"In a way I do. You explained everything. But there are some things that can't be changed by explanations."

"You mean there are some things that can't be forgiven, don't you?" he said in a hard voice.

"I don't think it's for me to forgive. It was Andrew who suffered. I can't forgive you on his behalf."

"For God's sake, Rae, put Andrew in the past, and live your own life. You don't owe him anything."

"I owe him loyalty. That will never change."

"And your idea of loyalty is to continue old enmities forever, is it? What good will that do him?"

"None. I know that. Let's say I'm doing it for my own sake. I told you, he was a wonderful father to me. I owe him better than this." She looked up to see him staring down at her, his face hard and set. "Giles, I'm sorry," she pleaded. "I know I should have thought of all this last night, but somehow I couldn't. I didn't mean to lead you on."

"To hell with that!" he snapped. He sat down beside her and took her by the shoulders, giving her a little shake. "Will you see sense?" he growled. "You can't put the clock back, and that's what you're trying to do. You think you can pretend that what's between us is only an illusion. But you know better. You know what it meant."

"It didn't mean anything," she said desperately.

"That's what you're going to tell yourself, is it? That's going to be the pretense? Rae, when are you going to stop living in Andrew Haines's world and face reality? The reality is us. The reality is *this.*"

His hands tightened on her shoulders, pushing her back onto the bed. In a moment his mouth had covered hers, silencing her gasp of protest. He began to pull open the thin silk, urgently caressing the bare flesh beneath, reminding her of sensations she wanted to forget because they could bring her only heartbreak.

He kissed her hungrily, with all the desperation of a man seeking to convey something for which he can find no words, and the temptation to yield to him was overwhelming. For a moment her hand hesitated on the verge of a caress. But then strength returned to her. She writhed desperately in his arms and managed to free her mouth. He loomed over her, and for a moment she thought he meant to overwhelm her completely.

But then he froze as though a hand of ice had touched him. His eyes were fixed on her desperate face. Slowly he released her and pulled away, moving like a man in a state of shock. Hurriedly Rae closed the dressing gown against him, fearful of what her burning flesh had revealed.

Giles sat on the edge of the bed, his hands clasped between his knees. His face was white.

"I'm sorry," he said in a strained voice. "I couldn't hurt you, Rae. Tell me you know that."

"I do," she said in a low voice.

"I wouldn't have—"

"I know," she said, aching to enfold him in her arms and ease his torment, but knowing that there was no comfort she could offer him now.

"I suppose I've been a great fool," he went on, still in that slow voice full of painful discovery. "But when you came into my arms last night I thought you understood that what matters is what we create ourselves. And all the time you were thinking—what? I don't understand you."

''I don't understand myself,'' she said shakily. ''I just know I can't see you again. I'll even leave Kinroy & Son if you're going to keep on coming there.''

''Dammit, I *want* you to leave that place! I've told you so a hundred times.''

''Yes, but you want to support me, and I can't let you.''

His face was haggard with the pain of rejection. ''You won't let me do anything for you, will you? Are you saying you still hate me?''

''No, I don't,'' she said quickly. ''But we have to break it off totally, and we can't do that as long as I'm taking money from you. Please stop coming into the firm, Giles, and don't contact me again.''

''So you can just go on exhausting yourself?'' he said with soft savagery.

''Giles, you can't help me.'' Rae spoke as gently as she could, but she couldn't escape the knowledge of what this rejection was doing to him. The things he'd told her about his childhood were still clear in her mind, and she knew the crosscurrents in his life were more complex than even she had suspected—more, perhaps than he knew himself. He had more than one reason for wanting to help her.

''No, I can't,'' he said at last, wearily. ''I can't if you won't let me.''

''I think I should go home now.''

''Have some breakfast, then I'll drive you.''

''No, I'd rather you didn't.''

''There's virtually no public transport from here on a Sunday.''

''Then I'll call a minicab.''

''Which will cost a fortune. Will you at least let me pay that for you?'' As she hesitated, he managed a strained smile. ''After all, I did promise to drive you home on Friday night, and then brought you here instead. You could make out a case that I owe you the fare home.''

''All right,'' she said, not because she believed in his argument, but because she couldn't bear to hurt him with another refusal and see the grayness come into his face.

Neither of them had any appetite for breakfast. Giles called a local minicab firm and they waited, nervously polite, till the car arrived. He opened the rear door for her and leaned toward her slightly as if he would have kissed her. But at the last minute he seemed to think better of it, and let her go without so much as touching her hand.

The apartment was freezing cold when she got in. She reminded herself that it had stood empty for two days, and hurried to put the heating on. She thought how dismal an electric fire looked after burning logs, then thrust the thought aside, fearful of an ominous tightening in her throat.

At least she'd caught up on her sleep, so it seemed practical to make good use of it. She got out her books and pored over them all afternoon and well into the evening. But perhaps she wasn't as well rested as she'd thought, because she seemed to be taking in very little.

She wondered if she ought to telephone Giles to let him know that she'd arrived safely. Surely that would be courteous? After ten minutes she'd convinced herself that it would be perfectly all right to call him. But she didn't.

At nine o'clock in the evening, a strange restlessness came over her. In the past, when he'd telephoned her, he'd usually picked this time, or just a little later. If he didn't call by ten o'clock she knew he wasn't going to.

She sat by the phone until midnight. Then she went to bed.

In the week that followed, Giles neither telephoned her nor came to Kinroy & Son. Rae found a kind of peace. It wasn't a happy peace, but finally she could begin to believe that the whole business was over. After eight years, she was free to draw a line through that part of her life and begin again.

On the Wednesday, she hurried back from her lunch five minutes late. Joan looked up sharply when she came in.

"You'd better get in there quick," she said, jerking her head toward Frank Kinroy's door. "The old devil's been snarling for you."

"It's only five minutes, for heaven's sake!"

"I don't think it's that. Mr. Blake called him about an hour ago. I put through the call. They were talking for about twenty minutes, then Kinroy slammed the phone down hard, came out here and bellowed for you. He's in a really nasty mood."

Before Rae could answer, the door crashed open behind her. Frank Kinroy stood there.

"Oh, there you are," he snapped. "Well, you can just get your things and get out."

"But... *why*?"

"Don't play innocent with me. You know damned well why. I've had Giles Blake on the phone. I couldn't believe my ears when he told me how insolent you'd been toward him."

"But—"

"Don't waste my time with denials. He gave me chapter and verse. He tried to get me on the phone this morning, and you wouldn't put him through, gave him a lot of rudeness. He called me while you were out at lunch. It was as much as I could do to stop him canceling the whole order. Do you know what that would mean to a firm this size? It could ruin me. So you're *out*, as of now. That was the only thing that would placate him."

"He asked you to fire me?" said Rae furiously.

"He *demanded* that I fire you if I wanted to keep the order."

"He can't do that," snapped Rae. "You can take him to court."

"Take *him* to court. Do you know who you're talking about? I threatened him with the law and he laughed, said he couldn't wait to see me in court and tell everyone a few—" Frank Kinroy broke off as if aware that this recollection wasn't helpful. Joan gave a smothered snort of laughter.

"Get out," said Frank Kinroy to Rae. "Get out now. I don't want to risk his coming in again and finding you here. I'll send your things on in the mail."

"All right," said Rae, recognizing that argument was useless. "But make sure my money's paid in full, and don't shortchange me as you shortchange your customers by giving them bad materials when they've paid for good; or as you shortchange the Revenue in a hundred little ways I know about, like the expensive heating system 'for the office' that was offset against the firm's tax bill, but which is actually warming your own home right now while Joan and I freeze in temperatures below the legal minimum."

"You can't talk to me like that," howled Kinroy.

"I can. You just made it possible. So while I'm enjoying my newfound freedom I might as well take the opportunity to tell you that it's only been the most dire necessity that has forced me to put up with your bullying, your meanness, your deceit, your laziness, your way of blaming your own mistakes on other people, your attempts at sexual harassment that would be disgusting if they weren't pathetic, and the smell of unwashed armpit that surrounds you like a halo."

"Get out!" he bellowed.

"It'll be a pleasure," said Rae.

The knock on her apartment door came promptly at eight o'clock. She opened it with the speed of someone who'd been waiting on edge.

"You're a brave man, coming here," she said severely.

"I know, I'm shaking in my shoes," said Giles. "Are you sure there isn't any boiling oil on the top of the door?"

"There would have been if I could have managed it."

He'd managed to surprise her again. As he came in she studied his face—he was actually happy. His eyes were full of the exhilaration of someone who'd got his own way against all the odds, and knew there wasn't a thing his opponent could do about it. But Rae put up a last-ditch fight.

"You might as well know now that I've been doing sums all afternoon," she said as she went to put on the coffee.

"So have I."

"I've been calculating my state benefits—"

"So have I. At least, my secretary has. I fed her your rough circumstances, and now I have a tolerably exact idea of what you can expect."

"Then you must see that you've been wasting your time. With the Social Security payments I'll get—"

"You'll starve. You know you will. So let's stop wasting time and get down to business."

"You've forgotten my escort work. Now I'll have my days free for study I can do several extra evenings—"

"Rae, let's get one thing clear here and now," he said firmly. "You've finished with that agency. Tomorrow you'll call them and take your name off their books."

"Oh, *will* I? Just who said you could give me orders?"

"You did. The other night."

"The other night does not give you the right to dictate my life."

"It gives me the right to keep you out of the clutches of other men, and it's a right I'm going to defend to the death. You are no longer for hire, and that is final! If you force me, I'll get you booted out of the agency by much the same methods I used with Kinroy, and don't think I wouldn't."

There was no doubt he meant it. His tone was still light, but she wasn't fooled. This was the predatory male asserting his possession of the female, prepared to do anything necessary, untroubled by scruples.

"Do you know what you are?" she fumed.

"I believe the commonly accepted term is male chauvinist pig," he said with a grin. "Go ahead! Throw it at me. It leaves me quite unruffled. Most of us are at heart, if you want the truth. If it brands me as a porker to want to see you living a life that's less exhausting and less fraught with danger than your present one, then so be it!"

"It isn't fraught with danger."

"Isn't it? What about those two louts who shoved past us on the stairs the first time I came here? They saw you wearing that mink. I have nightmares when I think of them breaking in here to rob you. I want you to move somewhere safer."

"No," she said. "I really can't do that, Giles."

"But you'll let me give you enough to live on comfortably, won't you? I won't ask anything of you. You won't have to see me. I won't even telephone, I promise. But let me do this for you, *please*."

She hesitated. It was so hard for her to sacrifice her stubborn pride. But when she looked at Giles she knew she couldn't refuse him again. She'd never seen him as he was tonight, his eyes full of happy confidence. It made no sense, and yet it made perfect sense. At the very moment he was promising to leave her alone he was full of unquenchable joy because he was with her now. She knew that because his joy echoed her own.

She thought of the bleak, lonely week that had seemed so long without him, of the arid peace that she'd told herself was all she wanted. She thought of the irrational leap her heart had taken this afternoon at the discovery that he hadn't forgotten her, after all, and she knew there was no way she could reject him and see the light die in him, and in herself.

"You haven't left me very much choice," she said.

"I haven't left you any," he said simply.

She smiled. "In that case—thank you."

He made a movement as if he would have seized her in a celebratory hug, but restrained himself at once. Rae flinched. Another moment and she knew she'd have gone into his arms. But Andrew's shadow still stood between them.

They looked at each other awkwardly until Giles said, "I think the coffee's ready."

"Yes," she said. "Sit down. I'll bring it in."

When they were seated and she was pouring he said, "I'm a bit surprised you're even talking to me. I expected at least a frying pan over the head."

"Well, you deserve it," she said wryly. "But as it happens, there's one thing I really am grateful for."

She described her last five minutes at Kinroy & Son, and Giles rocked with laughter.

"I hoped you'd take the chance to tell Kinroy a few things," he said. "I only wish I could have been a fly on the wall."

"I wouldn't have missed it for anything in the world," she said, chuckling. "I forgave you on the spot."

There was a small silence as though he was trying to decide whether to say something. At last he said, "Let's start being practical. Your head for figures is better than mine, so—"

Within minutes the table was covered in sheets of paper bearing figures that they examined together. She showed him her estimated budget, trimmed to the bone. He took one look at the bottom line and told her he proposed to pay her double the figure given there.

"I don't need anything like that much," she said, scandalized.

"That figure is ridiculous. It wouldn't keep a mouse alive, let alone someone in training for exams," he said.

"Yes, for exams, not for the heavyweight championship of the world," she protested.

"Now there you're wrong. The exams that will decide your life *are* the heavyweight championship of your world, and that's how you must approach them. Get up early, get plenty of sleep, take long bracing walks and eat steak."

"Is that what you did?"

"Except for the steak, yes. But you're right to ask me because I'm the expert. Rae, no one can tell you as much as I can about passing important exams. You're on the last lap, and you've got to pace yourself, build up your physical strength, because if your body is tired your brain won't function properly."

He got up and began to pace the room while he described the routine she should follow. He might have been instructing a jury in his beautiful dark bass that seemed designed to resonate throughout a courtroom. But Rae found she didn't mind. Giles's manner might be didactic but his whole attention was given over to her welfare. What was more, he was offering her the benefit of matchless experience gained in a hard school, and every word he spoke made sense. She found herself thinking what a good friend he'd make.

"All right," she said meekly when he'd finished. "I promise to do as I'm told."

He regarded her cynically, but all he said was "You've already had my promise to leave you alone. I won't trouble you. I won't even telephone. But I want your word that you'll call me if you're in any trouble. Night or day. Is it a bargain?"

"Yes, it's a bargain."

"Take care of yourself, that's all I ask. I'll give you the first check now, and after that I'll send them in the mail."

He wrote out the check. She was still reluctant to take so much, but he silenced all protest by saying, as he handed it to her, "Thank you, Rae."

"Shouldn't I be thanking you?"

"No," he said gravely, and she knew better than to ask him what he meant.

The next day she began to follow his routine, and almost immediately she felt better. She rose early, went for a brisk walk and returned to a hearty breakfast. By midmorning she'd settled down to study.

After lunch—"a proper lunch, mind you. No gulping a sandwich and giving yourself indigestion"—she'd take a break and do some shopping. Following Giles's instructions, she frequently bought steak, which she'd eat for her evening meal, and sometimes, remembering that she was in training for "the big fight," for breakfast, too. The late afternoon was given over to more studying.

She also spent some evenings studying. But occasionally she put the books aside, and relaxed with an undemanding television show, or read a crime thriller. "It wasn't what I did," Giles had said, "but it's what I should have done." And she was in bed by ten o'clock.

While she was following this regimen, her work made giant strides. Now that she was full of energy she found that everything came easily, and what she read stayed in her mind. In two weeks she'd revised the work of the past six months and recovered all the ground that she'd been losing.

Giles kept his word and made no attempt to contact her by so much as a postcard. But she thought of him often, and always with gratitude. From her new standpoint she could see how dangerously she'd been slipping behind, even perhaps to the point of failure. In her heart she thanked him again and again for his care of her. She thanked him for the generosity that made it possible for her to eat the best of everything, so that her strength grew daily. She even thanked him for the high-handedness that had made him force her to accept his help just in time.

Sometimes she'd take up the picture of Andrew and herself, offering up a silent plea for his forgiveness, not for accepting Giles's help, but for the way her thoughts about him were turning. If she could have talked to Andrew, she knew she could have explained the financial assistance and he'd have said, as Giles had shrewdly predicted, "Good for you! Get every last penny." But she could never have made Andrew see that she wasn't taking Giles's money in reparation, but because to refuse it would be to hurt him, and that was something she could no longer bear to do.

Nor could she have told Andrew about the dreams that haunted her, dreams of a kiss so sweet and gentle that she longed to believe it had really happened; or of the moments when she awoke with her body aching for the feel of him next to her, surrounding her, inside her.

Giles had said once that the man who loved her would know both heaven and hell. She didn't know if he loved her and didn't dare ask herself if she loved him, but she knew that they'd given each other heaven and hell. The heaven had been brief, yet so glorious that the memory would give her no rest till the day she died. The hell was this dreadful desolation of separateness.

Even this, perhaps, she could have coped with, but at last her thoughts took a cunning turn and told her that she ought to be worried about him. He cared for her, but who cared for him? Who concerned themselves with whether he was well or happy? Who looked below the surface of assurance and success to the lonely, troubled man beneath? The answer was nobody, because nobody understood him as well as she did. It was a sign of monstrous ingratitude that she'd let so much time go by without even finding out how he was. The very least she could do was telephone him tomorrow with a civil inquiry.

After that she fell asleep again, and slept soundly the rest of the night.

Nine

Telephoning Giles with a straightforward query about his health ought to have been a simple business, but it was mysteriously fraught with difficulties. Rae considered calling him as soon as she rose next day, but then thought he probably wouldn't want to be troubled when he was getting ready for work. She'd leave it till the evening.

But when she'd returned from her walk, the voice of the serpent whispered that if she left it that long she'd lose her nerve. She should do it now, while she had the impetus. She snatched up the receiver and dialed.

The phone rang twice before Mrs. Jones picked it up.

"Mrs. Jones? This is Rae Bonham. Is Mr. Blake still there, by any chance, or could you give me his work number?"

"I can, but he isn't there today. He's in court." Mrs. Jones named one of the outer London boroughs. "He left here an hour ago."

When she'd put the phone down, Rae sat, indecisive. Her longing to see Giles was overwhelming, and here was a perfect opportunity to see without being seen. She remembered the high, anonymous public gallery where she'd sat during the latter part of Andrew's trial. She could slip in, reassure herself that Giles looked well and slip out again. A perusal of the phone book turned up the court's exact address. It would take her about an hour to get there.

Suddenly she realized how long it was since she'd left her apartment for anything but shopping or exercise. While she'd been buried in her books, spring had arrived in full force. Her little bedroom was filled with sunlight. Her mirror revealed a face to which no serious attention had been paid for weeks. It was a fresh face, glowing with renewed health and energy, but she felt that a discreet touch of makeup to welcome the spring was called for.

She pulled open her wardrobe and selected her best day clothes. After all, she argued, this was a court and she should show respect for the process of law by dressing properly. The deep blue coat that she'd bought for half price at a sale three days ago was the smartest thing she possessed, and the fact that it accentuated the blue of her eyes was pure coincidence.

The area to which she was traveling turned out to be as down-at-the-heel as her own. She stared out the bus windows, growing more puzzled by the minute. Surely Giles's work lay among major cases in large courts. What could possibly bring him here?

She found the building without difficulty and approached the man on the desk in the big, echoing lobby.

"I don't know which court I want," she confessed, "but it's the one where Mr. Giles Blake is appearing."

"Court number five," he said, consulting a list. "Down that corridor, first on your left. It's got the number written on the door. The public gallery's immediately to your right as you go in."

"Thank you," she said, hoping she didn't sound as self-conscious as she felt.

A few minutes' walking brought to the door. She stood outside it, trying to still the irrational beating of her heart. But of course she was agitated, she told herself. She had good reason to dread courtrooms, but she'd soon get her nerves under control. She turned the knob slowly and went in quietly. Then she stopped, full of consternation at what she saw, knowing that she should have expected it.

The court was far smaller than the Central Criminal Court where Andrew had been tried, and the public gallery, instead of being up high, was raised only a few steps from the floor. She'd counted on being safely hidden from Giles's view, but he only had to turn his head to see her. Still, it was too late to back out now.

She edged her way slowly along the spectators in the gallery until she found an empty space next to a very young man who was watching the proceedings with the eagerness of a puppy. He edged away to make room for her.

"Thank you," she whispered.

The boy gave her a friendly grin, then returned his attention to the proceedings. Giles, severe and dignified in the black robe of the advocate, was on his feet, conducting a cross-examination. The sight of him gave Rae an odd feeling. The last time she'd seem him dressed like this he'd been a cruel-tongued enemy, destroying her father and her world. Since then she'd become so used to seeing him in conventional clothes that there was something almost shocking in his appearance now, and the memories it conjured up.

The past was still strong enough to make her feel a flash of sympathy with the man at Giles's mercy in the witness box, but it passed almost at once. She instinctively disliked the witness who was a rat-faced man with a self-righteous expression and a long body that seemed to be constructed entirely from hard, straight lines.

"Mr. Conway, I should like to go over that once again," Giles was saying with the same chill courtesy that Rae remembered from long ago. "You have told the court that on the day in question you were not—that is, you *were*—in a hurry, as it was the last day of the month and you were concerned that your report to head office..."

Giles had managed to resume the smooth flow of words, but he was furious with himself for the slip. He was sure that everyone in court would associate his momentary confusion with the sight of a figure in blue who'd edged her way along the front of the public gallery. With an abrupt, self-conscious movement he turned his back on the gallery and forced his mind to hold a steady course.

Rae knew a surge of relief that he evidently hadn't seen her. She whispered to the young man, "Who's the defendant?"

"There", he said, indicating a small elderly lady with a sad, defeated face. Rae's heart sank.

"Oh, no," she said. "I don't believe it. That poor little old lady can't have done anything."

"That poor little old lady is a notorious shoplifter," muttered the young man. "She's got a record as long as your arm. She's on a shoplifting charge now. Open-and-shut case. Everyone said the prosecution can't lose. But Blake never misses a trick."

"You mean," said Rae, speaking through the ache of misery that swept over her, "that he's out for his pound of flesh, even if it means persecuting an old lady like that."

"I beg your pardon?" the boy said blankly.

"Giles Blake—you said he's really throwing the book at her."

"No," he whispered. "Blake is *defending* her. That's what I'm trying to tell you. It looked like an open-and-shut case. She says she didn't do it, but with her record who's going to believe her? That's Conway, the shop manager in the witness box right now. Blake says Conway's under pressure from head office to get convictions against shoplifters, so he's trying to pin something on Mrs. Ridgeway because she's an easy target.

"He got really hot under the collar about it, says he's going to make Conway wish he'd never been born. Well, no one thought he had a snowball's chance in hell, but you listen to him."

Rae was in a daze. The relief of discovering that her worst fears about Giles weren't true was so great that she almost felt faint. But she forced herself to concentrate on the cross-examination, and soon recognized what she was hearing. She'd heard it once before, but under very different circumstances. Giles was going for the jugular.

"Mr. Conway," he said icily, "you are asking the court to believe that over such a distance you could make out sufficient detail to be quite certain, beyond a shadow of doubt, that Mrs. Ridgeway lifted a bottle of perfume no larger than two inches and slipped it into her bag. You were able to see all this despite the comings and goings of other customers in between..."

He was going for the jugular, but this time it was in the lower court, out of the spotlight, in a small case that would bring him no publicity and very little credit. This time it was in defense of a bewildered little woman who looked as if she had no idea what was going on around her, and didn't possess two pennies to rub together. Rae could have sung for joy.

"I put it to you, Mr. Conway, that you saw nothing at all; that you were under pressure from head office to secure a conviction; that you knew Mrs. Ridgeway had a previous record that would leave her ill equipped to stand up to any accusation of yours, and that when you saw her walk into your store that morning you thought Christmas had come early."

There was a murmur of laugher. Giles had the court in the palm of his hand. The wretched witness knew it, too, because he mopped his forehead.

"Mr. Conway—" Giles moved in for the kill "—I suggest that your entire story is a fabrication, manufactured to save yourself trouble. I further remind you that you are under oath, that there are serious penalties for perjury, and that this is your last chance to tell the truth with some semblance of willingness."

There was a silence. Then Conway burst out, "It's not fair! She's pinched from me before, but I couldn't catch her. Why shouldn't I...?"

It was all over.

The rest was a formality. The judge directed the jury to find the defendant not guilty, and at Giles's request awarded her exemplary damages against the store. Rae saw Mrs. Ridgeway's eyes open wide in disbelief. The verdict seemed to have bewildered her more than anything that had gone before. But then Giles looked at the old lady with a kindly, reassuring smile. Rae drew in her breath at that smile. She had a strange feeling, as though she'd just seen the missing piece of a jigsaw fitted into place.

Beside her the young man was jubilant.

"Did you see that?" he kept asking unnecessarily. "Did you see that?"

Out of the corner of her eye, Rae saw Giles go over to Mrs. Ridgeway. Colleagues slapped him on the back and offered their congratulations. He replied with absentminded courtesy, not taking his attention away from the old lady. At last, he took her arm and led her gently out of the court.

"Do you know Giles Blake?" said Rae, forcing her attention back to the boy.

"I should just say I do. He's my master."

"I beg your pardon?"

He chuckled. "I mean, I'm his pupil. I was only called to the bar a few months ago. For the first year you 'devil' for your master, and go and watch him work whenever you can. I was determined to see this case because he didn't have a thing going for him. Also, I want to make the most of being his pupil because it isn't going to last much longer."

"Why? Do you have to move on or something?" said Rae.

"No, it's him that's moving on. Hello, Blake."

Rae looked around and found that Giles had returned to the court and come across to them. She managed to greet him in a normal voice, but her mind was whirling. Giles was "moving on" to some place where he'd have to leave his pupil behind. That sounded as if he was leaving London. She felt as if she'd received a blow in the stomach.

The young man, whom Giles addressed as Forster, was enthusing about the case.

"The way you tripped him up about the times, and then you got him to contradict himself—"

"You don't really need to tell me, Forster," said Giles, with quiet humor. "I was here, too, you know."

Forster subsided, blushing.

"Do you two know each other?" said Giles.

"No, we just got talking," Rae told him.

"Miss Bonham, this is Timothy Forster, a fellow lawyer, as I expect he's told you. Forster, this is Rae Bonham, a friend of mine. Now be a good fellow and take yourself off."

Forster vanished obediently. Rae and Giles were left looking at each other.

"Congratulations," she said quietly.

"You should have told me you were coming."

"I only made up my mind today. I'm sorry—" This was addressed to someone who was trying to get past her.

"Let's get out of here," said Giles. "Can you wait for me in the lobby for a few minutes?"

"Of course."

He joined her in the lobby ten minutes later. Without his black robe, he looked like himself again.

"It's only a few minutes' walk to the car park," he said. "Shall I drive you home or . . . will you have dinner with me?"

"I'd love to," she said at once.

"It's still early," he said as he swung the car out into the traffic, "but by the time we've driven into the city center, the restaurants will just about be open. I can wine and dine you and still have you home for your early night."

He was telling her casually that his promise to make no demands still held good, dispelling the tension that he thought she might otherwise feel. It was a courteous gesture. Rae wished she knew how she felt about it.

"I'm playing truant today," she said lightly. "Didn't you prescribe the odd day off?"

"If I didn't, I should have. How are your studies going?"

She plunged into the subject, and it occupied them safely till they reached the center of London, where they could switch to the even safer subject of restaurants.

"Would you like a steak?" he said as they went past a steak house.

"Not another one," she said quickly. "I've been eating steak till it's coming out my ears. I really will be able to take on the heavyweight champion of the world soon."

He laughed and said, "Then I know just the place."

A few minutes later they were installed in a corner table of a quiet little Greek restaurant. While Giles studied the menu, Rae looked around her. She wondered if he'd chosen this place carefully to reinforce his message. The lighting was subdued, but not so dramatically as to suggest a romantic evening. There was no candlelight or flickering shadows. Here she could feel safe, if that was what she wanted.

When she, too, had looked at the menu, she looked up to find him studying her.

"You look better," he said.

"Thanks to you. I feel better than I have for months."

"Good. That makes everything right."

"And you?" she said politely. "I was wondering how you were. I called and Mrs. Jones told me where you were. I thought . . . I just thought it might be interesting to see you at work."

He looked at her to see if she'd intended an irony and she said hastily, "The other time doesn't count. It was so long ago."

In truth, she'd momentarily forgotten that she'd ever seen him at work before, he seemed so completely a different man.

"You came all that way just to see me?" he said, his eyes on her.

"Well, I . . . actually I was curious," she improvised cautiously. "When Mrs. Jones told me where you were, I could hardly believe it. I thought you only took on big cases in big courts. Or am I wrong about the kind of practice you have?"

"No, you're not wrong. You don't need me to tell you that I've come a long way since I prosecuted your father."

"You surely don't need to defend little old ladies up for shoplifting?"

"I don't need to, no." He was pushing his knife gently from side to side, not looking at her, and Rae saw that he was embarrassed. She waited, but soon was aware that he'd say no more unless she prodded him.

"Don't tell me she could afford your fees, Giles?"

"I didn't do it for nothing. I'm not a philanthropist," he said in an affronted tone, as if, she thought, amused, she'd accused him of something shameful. "My fee is paid by the Legal Aid Fund."

"But it can't be very much for that sort of case," she said. "There must have been more lucrative ways you could have spent the day."

He sighed, "Yes, there were, but... Look, I don't know how to tell you without sounding pompous. The fact is, I know people like Mrs. Ridgeway. I grew up among them. I know how close to the bone they live and how little hope they have. I know that if they get arrested everything's against them. When I see her, and people like her, I remember where I came from, and I say another prayer of thanks that I escaped."

"And that's how you say it?" she said, suddenly seeing the light. "That trial today—that was your prayer of thanks."

"In a way, yes. I like to give something back when I can. I have friends who work for the Citizens' Advice Bureau in that area. They sometimes send cases like Mrs. Ridgeway's to me—small, defenseless people who often find it very hard to get a really good lawyer."

"Someone like you, in fact," she said.

"Yes, someone like me. That sounds conceited, but to hell with it. Ma Ridgeway needed the best. She'd been nicked for something she didn't do, but with her record she didn't stand a chance."

Rae found herself smiling at his language. That this correct, formal man should refer to "Ma" Ridgeway being "nicked," as he might have done in his childhood, delighted her in a way she couldn't have explained. But behind her amusement she was deeply moved.

"The point," Giles was saying, losing his embarrassment as he warmed to his subject, "is that even a thumping crook is entitled not to be framed. But a lot of them don't get the best lawyers because the best have gone on to bigger and more spectacular cases."

"Is she really a thumping crook?" said Rae.

"The thumpingest." Giles grinned suddenly. "She even pinched my gold pen while we were having a consultation. I saw her shove it up her sleeve when she thought I wasn't looking. I felt like telling her I knew a fence who'd give her a good price for it."

"What's a fence?" said Rae, fascinated.

"A middleman who deals in stolen goods. If I stole your mink I wouldn't try to dispose of it myself. I'd take it to Honest Alf Wilson. He's one of the best in the business."

"*Honest* Alf Wilson?"

"He doesn't cheat his customers. Jake the Rake would be better still, but he's just gone down for a two stretch."

"Not one of your clients, obviously," said Rae, correctly interpreting this as meaning that Jake the Rake had gone to prison for two years.

"Yes, he was, actually. I did my best but they found him guilty. Still, considering what the police discovered in his possession, I don't think I need reproach myself too much."

If it had been any other man she'd have suspected him of making it up, but she knew this kind of fantasy would be beyond Giles. He was completely serious. Besides, there was nothing surprising in a lawyer having an acquaintance with the underworld. It was the way Giles talked about these people, with compassion amounting almost to affection, that amazed her. But perhaps, she thought, it shouldn't have done. They were the small people with whom he plainly still felt an affinity.

"I expect Mrs. Ridgeway has her own fence, anyway," she said.

"Probably. Her career in crime stretches back quite a bit. She does it to get the money to live."

"To live?" said Rae. "But can't she get state benefits?"

"She could," said Giles with a carefully straight face, "but she won't take them. She says she doesn't want charity."

Rae began to laugh and he joined her.

"She sounds a wonderful old girl," she said at last.

"She is. She's got as much courage as anyone I've ever known, but her view of life is a little cockeyed. I just hope the damages I got her will keep her straight for a while."

Rae was filled with happiness. His payments to herself might be passed off as an act of atonement, but this gift of time and understanding to people who could never repay him could only come from a generous heart, a heart whose depths she increasingly wanted to know. She wondered how she'd ever thought of Giles as a cold man.

His eyes were on her, and she knew from the light in them that he thought her lovely. She wondered if he'd say so, or if that would be to cross the strict boundary he'd set himself. But then the waiter came with their starters, and the moment passed.

"I'm glad we met today," Giles said when they were alone again. "There's something I've got to tell you, and I've been wondering how. I'm afraid you won't like it."

The plunging feeling inside her was like being in a plane that had hit an air pocket. It was true. He was going away. The happiness of a moment earlier vanished without trace.

"You don't have to tell me," she said. "Tim Forster said something."

Giles muttered something impolite. "I'll wring his neck. I wanted to tell you myself. I'm sorry. You shouldn't have learned about it like that."

"It hardly matters how I learned, does it? Do you know when?"

"Next week, actually. Like a coward, I put off telling you till the last moment."

"How do you feel about it?"

"Well, naturally, I'm delighted."

It was as though he'd punched her in the stomach. He had no regrets at leaving her. The beauty they'd shared had been, for him, no more than a night's pastime, after all. Because he was scrupulous, she had no doubt that the checks would still arrive on time, but he wouldn't give her another thought.

She knew she had no right to complain. It was she who'd said there could be nothing between them, ignoring his protests. Now it seemed he'd finally accepted her decision, and this he had every right to do. But it hurt that he was so blatant about his relief.

"Do you mind very much?" he said after a moment.

Now was the time to tell him she didn't mind at all, that she would forget him as gladly as he would her. But the words wouldn't come. Even if it cost her her pride, she'd force herself to be honest.

"Yes, I do," she said softly. "I'm surprised how much I mind." She gave a little self-conscious laugh. "There, I wasn't going to say that."

Giles's face was drawn. "Why shouldn't you say what you feel? It's just that I thought—that is, I'd hoped... Well, anyway, it's happened and there it is."

"Yes," she said dully. "How far away will you be going?"

"I beg your pardon?"

"This move, is it very far out of London?"

He stared at her. "Rae, what are you talking about? I'm not going anywhere."

"But... haven't we just been talking about your move?"

"What move?"

"The move Tim Forster told me about. He said he wasn't going to be your pupil much longer. I asked him if he was moving on and he said it was you who was moving on. Giles—"

His eyes were fixed on her face. "Is this what you've been talking about all this time? You thought I was going away somewhere?"

Her heart was thumping painfully. "Aren't you?"

"Of course not. What Tim meant— You mean you actually don't know?"

She shook her head. The lump in her throat was making it impossible to speak.

"I'm going to become a Queen's Counsel," said Giles. "I got it, after all. I've been wondering how to tell you."

If she said anything she knew she'd start crying. The relief was so sharp that she could only sit staring at him, careless of what her face was revealing.

"I should have known we were talking at cross-purposes," said Giles. "But you sounded as though you knew all about it. I knew you'd hate it and when you—"

He stopped as if something had just occurred to him, and Rae was suddenly awkward as she remembered how she'd told him she minded. To cover the moment she said, "I don't understand. What's this got to do with Tim Forster being your pupil?"

"A QC can't take pupils, that's all. Someone else is taking him over from me."

"But he spoke of your moving on."

"Well, by your account, you put that phrase into his mouth. He was using it metaphorically. When you're a beginner, being a QC looks like promotion."

"But isn't it?"

"In a manner of speaking. It's also a risk. These days I don't spend my whole life in court. Much of my work is giving opinions on cases that may never see the light of day. I make half my money that way, but when I'm a QC it'll be barred to me. I'll do court work and nothing else. So unless I can get a lot of extra court cases I'll suffer a big drop in income."

"But if it's such a risk, why do it?"

He laughed and colored, suddenly as self-conscious as a boy. "Well, to be honest, I think I'll get the extra work."

She'd recovered her poise now and was able to regard him ironically.

"Yes, I should think you just about might," she said, and they laughed together.

"Even if I had doubts, I'd still have done it. You see, most judges are created from QCs—not all, but most."

"And you've taken a step nearer the top of the tree, haven't you?"

"Yes. That's why I thought you'd object. I know how you feel about my ambitions."

"No, you don't," she said at once. "I think it's wonderful. Congratulations, Giles. I'm really glad I didn't prevent you from getting the appointment."

"Do you honestly mean that?"

"Of course I mean it. Things have changed. I couldn't go on hating you forever."

"I hoped you couldn't. Look—" He hesitated. "I suppose you wouldn't be interested in coming to see it happen?"

"See you made a QC? Can I?"

"Not the actual ceremony, no. But afterward all the new QCs have to go round the London courts, one by one, introducing themselves to the judges. They hold up the trials while we all pass through. If you wanted, you could sit in the last court and maybe we could meet later."

"That would be lovely. But what about Belinda and the children? Won't they be there?"

"No, it's a weekday, and Belinda feels they shouldn't lose any time from school."

His face was blank as he said this and Rae's heart ached for him.

"She's trying to separate them from you, Giles."

"I know. But I don't know what I can do about it."

"There must be something. You mustn't let her get away with it."

He made a grimace. "Anyway, will you come?"

"I wouldn't miss it for the world."

They talked about unimportant matters for the rest of the meal, but Rae knew they'd passed a milestone, as though their enmity was now officially dead and buried. She hardly knew what they said. She was intensely aware of him sitting near her. Even greater was her awareness of how long it was since he'd touched her, and how much she wanted him to touch her again. She'd thought she'd managed to subdue the memory of his caresses, but she'd been deluding herself. Those memories had only slept lightly. Now they were waking, as poignant as ever, as if it had been yesterday.

How could he sit beside her as indifferently as a stranger when their bodies had been so ecstatically united by desire? It was she who'd told him it had been a mistake, something that must never happen again, but now, illogically, she began to argue against herself. In his arms she'd known she was where she belonged. And it had surely been the same with him. That could never be forgotten.

Whenever Giles handed her something she held her breath, like a girl on her first date, lest his fingers brush hers. But, whether by accident or design, he avoided all contact, even when he held her coat for her to put it on as they left.

At the apartment block, Giles saw her to her front door. But when she invited him in for a drink he said, "I must hurry home. I have work to do. I'll call you in a couple of days and settle the details for next Friday. Good night, Rae." He hurried away.

Lying in bed that night, Rae unwillingly remembered Belinda's words. Giles believed a bargain was a bargain. He paid his dues to the last penny. He'd promised not to trouble her and he was keeping his word. But he troubled her nonetheless, in ways he didn't know about.

She remembered how he'd looked when he'd spoken about "the small, defenseless people." That was the second time she'd heard him use that phrase. He'd used it on the night of their first meeting to describe the people who'd been ruined by Andrew. She'd dismissed it then as rhetoric, but now she knew she'd been unfair. Giles defended the defenseless ones because nobody else would. He had a natural affinity with them, an understanding of their hopelessness, and he was filled with anger on their behalf. It was this anger, as much as ambition, that had made him attack Andrew so savagely.

Rae had always known that Andrew's activities had caused hardship to others but, preoccupied with her own struggle for survival, she'd barely had time to think of them. Now she knew she had to face the fact that he'd carelessly ruined people who weren't in a position to stand up to him. He hadn't been activated by spite or malice. In a way it was worse than that. He simply hadn't spared them a thought.

And neither did I, she realized, ashamed.

She'd defended Andrew because he'd been a wonderful father to her, and that would always be true. But in all honesty she knew that to be good to someone you loved was a kind of self-indulgence. There were thousands who'd also depended on Andrew, and who'd come off badly because they hadn't touched his heart.

But they'd touched Giles's heart, although he might not have expressed it that way. Behind his stern exterior he knew a human fellowship with life's victims. Rae had accused him of being without feelings, but now she asked herself honestly which of them had the greater compassion, and the answer shamed her.

Before she went to sleep she got up and switched on the light. She took the photograph of Andrew and herself from its place of pride on her desk and stood looking at it a long time. Then she kissed the handsome face that had once been everything to her, told him silently that she was sorry and said goodbye.

She wrapped the picture carefully in a soft scarf and put it away in the back of a drawer in her bedroom. She would always love Andrew, but he could no longer have first place in her life. Those days were over. Perhaps they'd been over for a long time, but she'd discovered it only today, when she'd sat in an obscure courtroom and watched Giles Blake move heaven and earth for Ma Ridgeway, a thumping crook who'd been nicked for something she didn't do.

Ten

Rae was in court early on Friday afternoon. The public gallery was raised above the well of the court, but she managed to secure a seat in the front row. She sat through the very boring trial of a machinery contractor accused of supplying faulty goods and was glad when it was over. There was a short pause, then a new set of lawyers entered. Looking down, Rae recognized Harris Bland, whom she'd met at the legal charity.

This trial was equally dull, but luckily it was short. Harris was just finishing his final speech when the judge interrupted him with, "Just one moment, Mr. Bland, please."

On the far side of the court a pair of double doors had opened. Rae could see Giles standing immediately outside in his black robe, not the robe that she'd previously seen him wearing, but the silk one of the Queen's Counsel. When there was silence Giles walked slowly into the court and faced the judge.

Rae leaned forward, trying to take in everything at once. Through the wide-open doors she could see the other new QCs. To her prejudiced eyes they made an uninspiring crowd. They were all older than Giles, and not one of them had his height, his austere good looks or his impressive bearing. Rae felt a surge of possessive pride. At the same time she knew an ache in her heart at the thought of what today must mean to him. He'd reached a pinnacle of achievement, but he had no one of his own there to share it.

"Mr. Giles Alexander Blake," said the judge, "Her Majesty having been pleased to appoint you one of her counsel learned in the law, will you kindly take your place within the bar."

Giles bowed to the judge, then turned and bowed to the other lawyers in the court, who all bowed back. Then he seated himself in the center of the front row of legal men to signify that he had taken his place.

"Do you move, Mr. Blake?" said the judge.

Rae knew, because Giles had explained it to her, that this wasn't a request for him to leave, but an invitation to start his career as a QC by making an application to the court. It was purely a formality, and Giles declined the invitation by rising, bowing again to the judge and walking to the door on the far side of the court to the one by which he'd entered.

The movement took him directly under the public gallery. His manner was grave and impeccably legal. He seemed totally absorbed in the solemnity of the occasion, and his handsome features had never looked so stern. Only the most observant could have noticed that as he neared the gallery he slowed by a fraction, just long enough for his eyes to flicker briefly upward, and that the severity of his features relaxed almost imperceptibly at something he'd seen there.

There were five more new QCs to go through the same procedure. One by one they passed through the court, and then the trial resumed. Rae knew that it would be at least half an hour before Giles was free to join her, so she stayed for the end of the trial and saw the verdict go to Harris, for the defense. Then she edged her way out of the gallery and went down to the big main lobby. There was no sign of Giles, so she sat down to wait.

After ten minutes she looked up just in time to see him appear at the end of the corridor. There was still a large crowd, and almost at once he was obscured from her vision. Then she saw him again. He was making his way down the corridor slowly, stopping to receive congratulations every few seconds.

Rae rose and began to advance to meet him, feeling suddenly shy. All at once she'd become intensely aware of her surroundings, the echoing gray stone of the ancient building, the walls lined with portraits of judges, the throng of men and women in the black robes that advocates had worn for centuries. This was Giles's world, where he was among his peers, people who respected him, but whom he also respected. He was at home here as she was not. She wondered what these learned and soberly dressed men and women would say if they knew Giles had invited the daughter of a convicted criminal to witness his moment of triumph. Was he perhaps already regretting it, seeing how out of place she was there?

The thought made her halt while she was still some distance from him. Absorbed in shaking hands, he didn't seem aware of her. But then he looked up and saw her and she knew that for him, as for her, the crowds had ceased to exist.

He hurried the last few yards, his eyes alight. When he stood in front of her she saw that his eyes were shadowed by anxiety as he waited for her first words, and she knew what those words had to be.

"I was so proud of you," she said, and saw the shadows replaced by light.

Neither of them thought it strange that she spoke as though he were hers.

"I was glad you were there," he said simply and reached out a hand to take hers.

"Blake, my dear fellow—"

They both turned quickly and saw Harris Bland bearing down on them.

"I've only just got out of court, or I'd have added my congratulations," said Harris, shaking his hand. He turned to Rae. "Sorry to barge in like this but— I say, haven't we met before? Yes... no," he corrected himself hastily. "Must be a mistake."

"There's no mistake," said Giles quietly. "This is Rae Bonham. You met her at the benefit dinner."

"Yes, of course," said Harris, recovering himself. "Nice to meet you again. Have you been watching in one of the courts?"

"Yes, yours actually," she said. "Congratulations, by the way, on winning the case."

He thanked her and they exchanged courtesies for several more minutes. After his first slip Bland had recovered his equanimity and his manner was perfectly composed. But Rae was aware of the puzzled sideways glances he was giving her, and the even more curious looks he was giving Giles. At last, to her enormous relief, Bland said goodbye and bustled away.

"We should have thought of something like that happening," she said. "He must have very sharp eyes to have recognized me."

"Oh, forget him," said Giles. "Let's get out of here."

"Giles—" she stopped him with a hand on his arm "—what kind of evening are we going to have?"

"How do you mean?"

"I mean, is it going to be like last time, dinner in a well-lit restaurant, polite conversation and a brotherly goodbye at my door?"

He looked at her for a moment as if trying to work out the question behind the question.

"What kind of evening do you want?" he said at last.

"Not one like that."

Still he hesitated. "You don't owe me anything," he said at last. "I told you there were no strings, and I meant it."

"I know. I believe you."

He gave her a faint smile. "I'm tempted to say something appallingly chauvinistic about women not knowing their own minds," he said.

"Well, you warned me you were a chauvinist," she said lightly. "And I could always reply with something old-fashioned about a woman's privilege."

He drew a ragged breath. "Rae, do you have any idea of the fire you're playing with when you talk to me like this? Don't you know that I want you badly enough to do something that would make it impossible for me ever to show my face here again?"

Laughing, she took his arm. "Let's go, then," she said, "while your reputation's still safe."

On the journey home Rae sat twisted sideways in the passenger seat, her eyes never leaving Giles. She made no move to touch him, but something in the intensity of her gaze must have got through to him because after a while he growled, "If you want us to have an accident, just keep looking at me like that."

"I'm sorry," she said unrepentantly.

Thereafter she sat demurely with her hands in her lap, but the composed expression on her face was in contrast to the turmoil within. She could think of nothing except how much she wanted him. His hands on the steering wheel reminded her of his touch in the darkness.

How straitlaced, even puritanical, he was in the light, she thought, remembering his unease when she'd taken the initiative and began to undress him. But how different he was when the light was extinguished. It was as though the darkness was a cloak of invisibility, bestowing on him the freedom to become another man, or perhaps the man nature had always meant him to be.

Fragments of old fables came back to her, fables of goblins and monsters, of enchantment, both good and evil. Many of those tales concerned human creatures fallen under spells, condemned to live disguised as animals by day and become themselves only for a few brief hours at night. Although children's stories on the surface, they often derived from folk myths as old as time, which embodied adult truths.

To her, Giles was like a man cursed in childhood by an evil spell that imprisoned him by day and only freed him to be his true self when there were no eyes to see. Now, as for centuries past, there was only one power strong enough to break the spell.

It was dusk when they reached Giles's house, which was in darkness. Not a single light shone to welcome them.

"Mrs. Jones took the weekend off to visit her brother," said Giles.

Rae thought of him as he might have been tonight, arriving here alone on his day of triumph, to find the house empty, spending the evening poring over papers.

The moment they were inside, Giles reached for Rae and pulled her into his arms. She raised her mouth to meet his and felt the touch of lips she'd longed for all through the lonely weeks. They were both still wearing their outdoor clothes, and several thicknesses of material separated them. Even so, Rae could sense his raw need, the echo of her own.

They kissed each other hungrily, trying to savor everything at once. The urgent pressure of his tongue parted her lips and she went into a spin of delight as he explored the inside of her mouth. With one arm he held her. With the other hand he caressed her face even as he kissed it, then ran his fingers through her hair, pulling it loose, tangling the soft strands.

"Rae," he murmured huskily when he could speak. "Rae... if you hadn't wanted me... I'd have gone out of my mind."

His mouth cut off any reply she might have made, but she was almost beyond coherent thought. She'd thought she'd had herself under control, remembering the last occasion, when she'd paced everything slowly at the outset. But then she'd been exploring this man for the first time, discovering his depths and her own, having no idea what lay in wait for her. Now she knew the hidden secrets of his sensuality, what he could make her feel that no other man could, and what they could do together. As she remembered all that, her body was in a fever of anticipation. It had known sensations it could never forget, and it was crying out to know them again.

"I was afraid you'd turn me down," she said when she could speak.

"Not a chance," he said against her mouth before taking it again, the forceful movements of his tongue making a dozen promises of delight to come.

When she came up for air next time she murmured, "A bargain is a bargain."

He teased the soft skin of her neck with his lips. "What damned bargain?"

He'd begun to nibble gently at her earlobe. Ripples of excitement swept through her, down the length of her body, her arms, her legs, making her toes and fingertips tingle. She managed to gasp, "You were going to stay away from me—remember?"

"I *did* stay away," he said savagely. "You're the one who didn't."

"Oh, yes," she said, as though only just remembering.

Abruptly he pushed her back against the wall.

"Rae, what is this?" he demanded. "Are you telling me you've changed your mind?"

She shook her head, her eyes dancing.

"No," she said. "I guess I'm just incurably weak-willed. You've no idea how nice it is to discover that *you* are, too."

"I'd have managed...somehow...if you hadn't walked into the courtroom the other day," he growled. "Do you know you almost made me lose the case?"

She put her hands on his shoulders and began to caress his neck and jawline gently with her fingertips in a way that strained his control to the utmost.

"I thought you didn't even know I was there," she whispered.

There was a silence, broken only by his ragged breathing. He was fighting to speak. His voice finally came huskily through the constriction in his throat.

"I knew from the first moment. I've got eyes in the back of my head where you're concerned." He pulled open the buttons of her coat and gave a sigh, almost of relief, as he encountered the curves beneath. "I'd know you in a crowd of a million," he groaned. "Poor Ma Ridgeway almost ended up in jail because I was thinking how much I wanted to—*Rae*!"

Beneath the coat his hands were trying to touch her everywhere at once. She wriggled to make it easier for him.

"Don't worry," she murmured in a voice that hovered on the brink of a chuckle. "Everything's in the same place as last time."

"That's good, because I have plans for all of it."

"Mmm, I have plans, too."

"The same ones, I hope."

"No," she said in a considering voice. "My plans are slightly different. We'll talk about them later."

"Are you playing games with me?" he demanded suspiciously.

"Oh, but you'll like my games. I promise."

His hands met behind her waist, crushing her against him.

"I'm not playing games," he said, lowering his head purposefully.

After a few moments he began to draw her up the stairs. She went with him in the circle of his arm, not seeing where she was going because she was concentrating on keeping her mouth on his.

"We're both still fully dressed," she said breathlessly when they reached his bedroom door.

"That can soon be remedied," he growled, taking her coat from her and tossing it onto a chair. She reached for the light switch but he stayed her and pulled her back into his arms, his fingers fumbling for buttons and zippers. Rae gasped as she felt his hands at last on her bare flesh. Then, quickly she began to remove her clothing herself because she was more adroit than he.

When she'd finished she found that he'd shed his own clothes and was waiting for her in bed. Before she'd finished lowering herself beside him, his arms were around her, pulling her close, then closer still. The hairs on his body rasped against her silky skin and she writhed against him, enjoying the wildly erotic sensation.

Her loins were heavy with a deep, slow, throbbing. It had started in the lobby that afternoon when she'd seen him coming toward her, and had become more powerful when she knew they were going to make love. It had been growing ever since, and now it was taking her over, becoming almost unbearable in its intensity.

She was burning with expectation and when he slipped a hand between her thighs, asking her silently if she were ready for him, she moaned fiercely, "Yes, *yes*!"

It was as though the words had ripped the lid off a powder keg. He covered her in one swift movement, easing himself between her legs. As she felt him become one with her, Rae let out a long shuddering sigh. His hard, muscular body felt so good on top of her, inside her. Mindlessly she began to rock her hips back and forth, meeting him, receding, meeting him again, in a voluptuous rhythm that grew in strength. Flames licked her. The fire was reaching its height, consuming her totally, leaving behind nothing but ashes and emptiness.

She found she was holding him closely, one hand splayed on his broad back, the other curved about his head. His face was buried against her neck. They lay like that for a long time.

"Are you asleep?" she said at last.

He raised himself on one elbow.

"I'm not so ill mannered, I promise," he said, with a faint smile. "I was trying to pretend it hadn't finished."

"Yes, so was I."

"You're not sorry?"

"No, I'm not a bit sorry. You were right. It was silly of me to think I could turn the clock back."

He rolled onto his back, pulling her with him so that her head was pillowed on his shoulder and his arm encircled her.

"I feel as if I could go to sleep now," he said in a voice of utter contentment. And in another moment he had.

Rae dozed against him for an hour. They awoke at almost the same moment and lay, warm and blissful, until she sat up suddenly.

"What's that noise?" she said.

"I think it may be my stomach protesting at being empty," said Giles. "I've eaten nothing since last night."

"You went out without breakfast just because Mrs. Jones wasn't here? I thought your mother house-trained you," she teased.

"It has nothing to do with Mrs. Jones. In fact, she was here this morning. I just couldn't get anything down. I was as nervous as a cat."

She wondered how she'd ever thought him a hard man. "What shall I get for you?" she said, kissing him tenderly.

"Not a big meal—unless you want one yourself. A light snack for me, please."

"Wait here." She switched on the bedside lamp and slithered out of bed. "Where can I find one of your dressing gowns?"

"Why worry? You're fine as you are," he said, looking at her with relish.

"I can't walk around the house naked. It isn't warm enough," she said laughing.

And besides, she thought, if you want a strip show you're going to have to give me one, too. The sheet covered him to the waist, revealing a broad, dark-haired chest, and no more.

Opening a wardrobe, she found the red silk dressing gown she'd worn before, but when she'd slipped it on her feet were still cold. Although spring had come, the weather was unseasonably chilly and the central heating was rather low for her taste. She could hardly walk around wearing nothing but a dressing gown and outdoor shoes.

"Where do you keep your socks?" she asked.

"My socks? Woman, is nothing safe from your predatory instincts? In the top drawer just behind you."

She found a pair of long socks and slipped them on her feet. Then she went downstairs to forage in the kitchen. She toasted some bread and made enough scrambled eggs for two. A pot of hot coffee completed the meal, and she carried it all upstairs on a tray.

She found Giles out of bed, dressed in the brown dressing gown. While she'd been gone he'd straightened the bed and pulled out a low table. Now he relieved her of the tray and helped her unload its contents onto the table.

"The perfect choice," he said when he saw the scrambled eggs.

They picnicked, sitting on the floor. To Rae's satisfaction, he scraped the plate as if famished. She became so preoccupied with watching him that she allowed a crumb of egg to fall from the fork and land between her breasts. When she'd retrieved it, she looked up to find Giles looking at her, frankly riveted.

"It's ridiculous," he said defensively. "We've been lying together naked. I've seen what you look like, yet I've been trying to peer down your cleavage like a sex-starved schoolboy."

She chuckled and pulled the edges tightly together, cutting off everything from view.

"Spoilsport," he complained.

"Voyeur!" she teased.

"If you *will* sit there half dressed... I don't know how I kept my mind on my food."

"Anyway, I've never seen what you look like," she said indignantly. "You won't let me put the light on."

He reddened slightly. "That's different."

"No, it isn't. I'm just as much entitled to be a voyeur as you are." He didn't answer this, and after a moment she said gently, "They're going to give women the vote any day now, you know."

He laughed but still looked uncomfortable.

"I suppose you think I'm a ridiculous prude," he said at last.

"Just a little old-fashioned," she said kindly. "But you partly explained it when you told me what your mother used to say about 'acting silly.' You find it very hard to let go when the light's on, don't you?"

"Almost impossible," he said frankly. "But to be fair to my mother, it's not entirely her doing. When people are as poor as we were they tend to live in cramped accommodation. Living on top of each other does develop inhibitions.

"It wasn't so bad for us because there were only two of us, although even we were often very squashed. But I knew large families living in two rooms. If you can't afford to put walls between you, you protect yourself with prudery instead."

She regarded him with her head on one side.

"What you need," she said thoughtfully, "is to be well and truly seduced."

"I thought I had been," he said with a faint smile.

"Oh, that," she said dismissively. "I mean really seduced, by a thoroughgoing *hussy*."

His eyes were fixed on her. "I'm not... quite sure I know what you mean," he said uncertainly.

"Then it's time you found out."

The little table was on castors. With one push she sent it rolling away into a far corner. Now she had all the space she needed.

A small radio stood by the bed. Rae switched it on and twiddled the knob till she came across some modern jazz—smoky, languid, full of the atmosphere of nighttime and dim lighting. Then she rose slowly to her feet, stretching as elegantly as a cat.

"A moment ago," she went on, "you said I was more alluring with clothes on than off."

"That isn't *quite* what I said," he put in hastily. "More tantalizing, let's say."

"Exactly." She seated herself on a chair close to him. "And the secret of seduction is to tantalize—not just removing your clothes, but doing it in the right way, like this."

Allowing the dressing gown to gape open slightly she raised one long leg, clad in the heavy, masculine sock. She slid her fingertips under the sock's ribbing and began to ease it slowly down her leg in a stylish imitation of a striptease artist. Giles watched her, grinning with pleasure.

"Aren't you supposed to use silk stockings for that?" he said.

She came out of character long enough to say, "Yes, but I couldn't find any in your sock drawer."

He laughed and she went back into her act. She was stripping the leg that was nearer to him, turning her shoulder toward him so that she could drop her head and hide her face, all but the eyes. Slowly she lowered and raised her eyelids in a theatrical parody of enticement.

Giles watched her with a smile on his lips. He was enchanted by the sight of her clowning, which he'd never seen before. He'd known she could be cruel, passionate and vulnerable. But until this moment he hadn't known that she could be funny. That was all this was, he told himself—a good joke.

And yet he found that it was having a disconcerting effect on him. As she raised her leg high in the air, drawing the sock off the end, the dressing gown slid backward down her thigh, almost revealing the curve of her behind, but not quite. He fought down the temptation to lean forward in case she laughed at him.

The music throbbed softly. Gradually the sock slid from her toes and she twirled it round her head before tossing it into a far corner of the room. Now Rae was on her feet, placing the other foot on the chair, toe pointed. She stood there a moment, looking at him from under heavy lids, rocking gently back and forth in time to the leisurely beat coming from the radio. The soft gyrations of her hips were a subtle echo of the rhythm of their loving. Giles was too far beyond precise thought to analyze this, but he felt something catch in his throat, and his breathing became ragged.

With torturing slowness Rae eased the sock down toward her ankle, while her eyes never left him. As the heavy wool went lower and lower, Giles realized that he'd never noticed before what delicately lovely legs she had, how slender and feminine was the ankle that was being revealed, inch by inch.

It was off, but instead of tossing it away she took the other end in her hand and held it high above her head while she swayed about the room, waving her hips to the soft, insistent beat, in a manner that had him fearing to blink lest he miss something.

Without warning she threw the sock at him. It landed across his chest and at once he sat up sharply, shattered by the sensation that had gone through him. It was one of his own socks, for pete's sake. Yet the sudden contact had been like a charge of electricity.

But it was no longer his own. It had entirely lost its character as a masculine garment belonging to himself. It had been in contact with her flesh, and by the intimate act of removing it for his benefit she'd imbued it with her own seductiveness. He touched it as reverently as if it had indeed been a silk stocking.

Now her fingers were pulling at the belt, working it loose. Giles's eyes were fixed on the belt, and his complete stillness was more eloquent than any movement. The knot was untied, the ends dropped, the edges of the garment fell two inches apart and were drawn swiftly back together. Rae's eyes met his. Laughing, she made as if to retie the belt.

But he was too quick for her. He made one swift lunge forward and just caught the end before she stepped back. He took determined possession of it, sliding it easily out of the loops.

"No cheating," he said.

Rae's answer was to drop her hands and let the edges of the gown fall wide apart, but at the same moment she twisted so that her back was to him. She gave a heavy-lidded glance over her shoulder and twitched the silk aside, allowing him a flashing glimpse of thigh. Giles's hands tightened on the belt he was holding. He wondered if she knew how close she was to being tossed unceremoniously onto the bed.

Still with her back to him, she'd begun to slide the silk garment off her shoulders and downward. Inch by inch it crept toward her waist. She made a half turn that allowed him a fleeting glimpse of one lovely breast before she drew her arms together at the front. The move concealed her breasts but caused the silk to tighten at the rear, outlining every curve of her bottom as she began to shimmy toward the door, which stood open.

At the very last moment she slipped the garment off entirely before disappearing. As Giles rose to his feet in instinctive protest one bare arm reappeared to drop the dressing gown on the floor, then vanish. From outside he heard her soft laughter.

The sound galvanized him. In one movement he reached the door as it was beginning to close, wrenched it back and pulled her straight into his arms. His head descended purposefully, and for a long time neither of them could speak.

When he felt her fingers moving at his waist he tensed instinctively, but did nothing to stop her. Then the belt was loosened and she was running her hands over him, gradually easing off the dressing gown until he was as naked as she.

She took him by the hand and led him to the bed, looking back and smiling at him. Eve, he thought, must have looked like that as she led Adam to the tree of forbidden fruit. As a punishment they'd been cast out of Eden. Giles knew that if he was to pay for this moment for the rest of his days it would make no difference. He'd still follow wherever she was leading and count it worth the cost.

She drew him down beside her on the bed and pushed him gently over onto his back. She made love to him with her hands and her lips, rejoicing in the beauty of this marvelous male body. She could feel him trembling under her touch and knew she didn't have much time. She could see that her striptease had been totally effective, and at any moment the urgency of his arousal would become greater than his control.

She moved swiftly, sliding over him before he knew what she meant to do, taking him inside her, moving against him in a way that left him no choice but to yield to the explosive desire that had built up in him. When their moment came, his arms drew her irresistibly down onto his chest, and she heard the violent pounding of his heart beneath her ear.

She didn't move as her own blood began to slow its mad race. She wondered what she'd see when she looked up at him. Anger that she'd stormed his defenses? A drawing back from her, to reestablish the reserve she'd stripped away? Had she taken a risk she'd regret? Then she heard his voice murmuring in her ear, "You *are* a hussy." The note of pleasure was unmistakable.

She pulled back and looked eagerly into his face. He was smiling at her, and his hands were gentle as he pushed back a strand of hair from her face.

"A shameless, abandoned woman?" she queried hopefully.

"All that," he said in a decisive tone.

She fell back onto the bed beside him, then sat up and surveyed him with frank admiration. Her hands had told her of his hard, lean torso and narrow hips. She knew the feel of his heavy muscular legs against her own slim ones, and deep inside her she was still achingly aware of the power of his loins. All her senses had conveyed to her the unmistakable knowledge of male strength and beauty, and now she knew they hadn't lied.

"Will I do?" he asked a shade defensively.

"Mmm . . . ?" She appeared to consider the matter. "Just about."

"Thank you. Now come here."

She went into the curve of his arm and snuggled against him.

"I'm beginning to understand that cryptic remark you made earlier," he said, "about the games we were going to play."

"I told you you'd enjoy my games."

"Oh, I enjoyed them. Of course, if I was suspiciously inclined, I could ask some questions about how you came to be so expert at striptease."

"Rubbish! Anyone who's ever been to the movies knows how to do that. And while we're being suspicious, tell me something. Is it entirely a coincidence that Mrs. Jones just happened to want to visit her brother on your big day? It seems an odd sort of time for her to pick."

She wriggled away to get a better look at him, and could have laughed aloud at the expression on his face.

"Mrs. Jones's brother suffers from poor health," he said with the air of a man choosing his words carefully. "It troubles him at unexpected moments."

"Unexpected's the word. I'll bet Mrs. Jones found it totally unexpected to be given the weekend off; almost as unexpected as her brother found it when she walked in on him."

"What are you insinuating?" he said warily.

"I'm not insinuating anything. I'm saying straight out that you, Mr. Giles Alexander Blake, QC, one of Her Majesty's 'counsel learned in the law,' are the biggest fraud. I didn't take you by surprise tonight, at all. You planned this whole thing."

"I didn't *exactly* plan it," he said hastily. "I just thought that perhaps... when we talked last week you said... at least, you implied... that is, I thought you meant—" He read the unholy glee in her eyes at the sight of him tying himself in knots and finished resignedly, "Well, a man can hope, can't he?"

Laughing, she threw herself into his arms. He held her tightly as though he'd just discovered something precious. She curled up next to him, more blissfully happy than she could ever remember being. She could hear the beat of his heart. It was keeping exact time with her own. She began to take deeper breaths, trying to time her breathing with his, so that everything should reflect their perfect harmony. A sleepy warmth was stealing over her.

"You know," he murmured into her hair, "when I was younger I used to plan for this day. It was the dream that kept me going when I was tired and cold and hungry. The one thing I could never quite decide, though, was how I was going to celebrate on my first evening. I went through a thousand possibilities, but none of them came anywhere near the truth."

He stopped as he heard her give a faint mutter. Her head had fallen forward, suddenly heavy. Craning his neck, he just managed to see that her eyes were shut. When he was quite certain that she was safely asleep, he drew her closer and kissed the top of her head.

"None of them was as beautiful as the truth, my darling," he whispered.

Eleven

Rae was alone when she woke. There was a soft light in the room, and she slipped out of bed and went to the window. It was early in the day and the sun was just coming up, a fresh spring sun that heralded a bright morning. She wanted to throw the window wide and tell the world that it was the bright morning of her love.

How long had she loved him? Since she'd seen him at Mrs. Ridgeway's trial? Since their last time in this house when she'd seen the pain in his face as she rejected him? Since the first night? Did it matter? She loved him now.

She hurriedly put on some clothes and went downstairs to find him moving about in the kitchen. He looked up when he heard her, and she saw the wariness in his eyes as if he feared another rejection. She went to him at once, putting her arms round him and felt his tension ease.

"The kids are coming today," he said as he made the coffee.

"Do you want me to go?"

"No, I want you to stay. You know what to say to them."

"But you've known them much longer than I have," said Rae. "How come you don't know what to say to them by now?"

"It was different when they lived here all the time. We encountered each other on and off, and Belinda was there to help me out. But now they come for a solid stretch of time and it's just me and them.

"You can share a house with someone for years without realizing how superficial your relationship actually is. Suddenly I've discovered that I don't really know them. I want to reach them, but I can't. I feel the time slipping away, and I feel *them* slipping away. But I don't know what to do."

"I'll gladly stay, if it makes you feel better."

Over toast and coffee she said, "What had you planned to do today?"

"I hadn't thought. I leave it to them to suggest something."

She pointed to an advertisement in the morning paper, which had come through the door a few moments earlier.

"There's a fun fair on Hampstead Heath," she said. "I loved fun fairs when I was a child, and I've never quite gotten over it."

"Fine," he said in evident relief.

Half an hour later, when Rae had just stepped out of the shower in the bathroom, there was a ring at the door. The bathroom window looked out onto the back garden, and after a few minutes she saw Melanie and James on the lawn. From downstairs she could hear voices. Belinda's was cool and didactic, the voice of a woman who has only to state her wish to gain it. Giles sounded as though he was struggling to control his temper.

Mostly the sound was blurred, but just before the front door closed Rae heard Belinda say, "I do hope you won't upset them by making an issue of this, Giles. These visits are quite enough of a strain on them as it is."

Rae clenched her hands, furious at the implied threat and what she knew it would be doing to Giles. She waited until she'd heard the car drive away before going downstairs.

"What is it?" she said when she saw Giles's face, black as thunder.

For answer, Giles went to some pegs on the wall where the children's coats now hung. He turned each coat so that Rae could see the name tags sewn into the insides of the collars. They read Melanie Martin and James Martin.

"Martin?" she said indignantly. "You mean she's . . . ?"

She was silenced by a gesture from Giles. The children were returning. They greeted Rae with enthusiasm. Even the normally quiet James looked distinctly pleased to see her. Melanie bounced about with an exuberance that escalated to riotous joy at the news that they were going to a fun fair.

The journey to the heath, with the children in the back of the car, provided no opportunity for talking. But once they were at the fair Melanie and James pleaded to go on the first merry-go-round they saw.

"Can she change their names like that?" said Rae as they stood together watching the horses spin past.

"Not legally, no," said Giles. "Not unless I give my consent. I can take her to court and force her to change them back. But she's counting on my not being prepared to do that. She's just had John Martin's baby and she says it's 'nicer' for all three children to have the same name."

"That's just an excuse to move them another step away from you," said Rae indignantly. "Are you going to let her get away with it?"

"What do you suggest I do? Subject my children to a court battle?" said Giles bitterly.

Rae said no more. She wanted time to think.

As soon as she'd jumped down from the merry-go-round, Melanie hopefully suggested that the roller coaster ought to be their next port of call. It was an unusually impressive specimen, with long, steep hills down which the cars plunged at breakneck speed, to the accompaniment of bloodcurdling screams from the occupants. James immediately countersuggested an ice cream, and Giles supported him with a haste that made Rae suppress a chuckle.

Over the next hour, Melanie showed herself possessed of great ingenuity and persistence. She happily accepted an ice cream, a toffee apple, a ride on the bumper cars and a trip through the hall of distorting mirrors. But between each item she relentlessly reintroduced the idea of the roller coaster. With equal perseverance, the men of the family, who seemed to be made of less stern stuff, sought to distract her.

"Am I ever going to get on the roller coaster?" she asked at last plaintively.

"You're not going to give up, are you?" said Giles.

She shook her head. Giles made one last effort.

"It looks awfully big to me. Some of those descents are very steep. You'd leave your tummy a mile in the air."

"That's the *fun*," she told him severely. "*I'm* not scared."

She emphasized the last words just enough to be provocative and Giles regarded her cynically.

"Come on, then, all of you," he said, recognizing defeat.

"Look," said Rae quickly. "I don't really like roller coasters. I think I'll stay here. Perhaps James could keep me company."

"Yes," said James at once.

Years spent professionally weighing every word before he uttered it kept Giles silent long enough to notice the pallor of his son's face and the way he edged closer to Rae. He looked down at Melanie.

"It looks like it's just us two," he said, and the little girl's face glowed.

Rae pointed to an ice cream stall.

"James and I will be over there when you guys have finished," she said. "Don't hurry on our account. Have as many trips as you want," she added mischievously.

Giles gave her a look that consigned herself, Melanie and the entire race of women to perdition. Then he went off with his hand on his daughter's shoulder.

Twenty minutes later, she and James wandered over to the roller coaster just in time to see a car bearing Giles and Melanie come to a halt. A good-natured argument seemed to be taking place, which ended with Giles lifting his daughter bodily out of the car.

"It was wonderful," said Melanie, bounding over to them. "We had *three* rides. I could have stayed on all night." She took her father's hand and added kindly, "But Daddy was turning a bit green, so we got off."

"Thank you, darling," said Giles. He took Rae's arm and murmured, "Remind me to strangle you."

They found an open-air café near a small lake. The children fell on their food as if starving. Giles seemed unable to face anything stronger than coffee. When they couldn't eat any more, Melanie and James took the remains of some cake and went to the edge of the water to feed the ducks.

"My daughter must have a stomach lined with cast iron," complained Giles. "How she could eat on top of ice cream, toffee apple and three trips on that devil's machine—" Words failed him at the memory.

"Are you recovered yet?" Rae asked, chuckling.

"I won't recover this side of Christmas. But it was worth it. Thank you, Rae. I've never had a day like this with them before."

"You could have brought them here without me."

"I wouldn't have thought of it. Besides, it wouldn't have been the same. You make all the difference."

He reached out a hand and took hers, but after squeezing it he drew back at once. If they'd been alone she knew he'd have taken her in his arms, but in this public place even that slight gesture cost him an effort. Rae wondered if he'd ever manage to tell her that he loved her, or whether she'd have to take that on trust. It never occurred to her to doubt that he did love her. What had happened was too overwhelming to be on her side alone. She smiled at him, full of warmth and happiness.

"Giles, what are you going to do about the children's names? Are you going to let Belinda get away with changing them?"

"What else can I do?" he said despairingly.

"You can fight. Tell her you'll take her to court if you have to. My guess is that she'll back down. If she really has broken the law—"

"She has."

"Then she can't risk your taking her to court. She'd come out of it looking too bad. She's bluffing."

"Suppose she isn't. What would a court battle do to the children?"

"Would they actually have to appear in court?"

"No."

"Then I don't think it'll harm them half as much as if you do nothing."

"What do you mean? How can it harm them if I do nothing?"

"If you fight they'll know they matter to you, that you care about being their father. If you do nothing, Belinda will tell them that you are indifferent."

Giles's eyes kindled. "Yes, she damned well will, too."

"She's just testing her strength. If you give in, she'll take something else away from you, and then something else, and something else. Your only chance is to stand up to her now.

"If there's a row it'll be a bit unsettling for a while, but in the long run it won't matter. If you give up without a struggle they'll think you don't care, and that will mark them for life—especially Melanie."

He was silent for a while, his eyes showing his indecision.

"Giles, you once told me that I should take your advice about pacing my studies, because you were the expert. Well, on this subject, *I'm* the expert. I'm telling you, from my own experience, that if a girl grows up knowing she's important to her father she can go out into the world and deal confidently with every man she meets."

He smiled wryly. "Yes, I can't remember ever seeing you at a loss. I'd like Melanie to have something of what you have."

He was quiet for the rest of the day. He gave Rae no indication of whether he meant to take her advice, and she didn't press him, knowing that it was a hard decision for him to make. Once or twice she saw him looking at his children with a puzzled frown that seemed to deepen when his eyes fell on Melanie. It wasn't lost on Rae that the little girl's attitude to her father was strangely protective, as though she understood, by instinct, the difficulties he had in reaching out. She had no doubt that the kind of break Belinda was trying to cause would damage the child, and for her sake, as well as for Giles's, Rae was ready to do everything she could to prevent it.

They arrived home to find Belinda's car outside the house. She was standing beside it looking impatiently up the road. With her newly slender figure, she looked even more elegant and coolly poised then before. Her eyes raked Rae as the family got out of the car.

"I'm sorry," said Giles. "I forgot Mrs. Jones wouldn't be here to let you in."

"Yes, you might have made a little more effort to be on time," said Belinda with a deadly smile. "My goodness, you two, what's happened to you? You look like a pair of ragamuffins."

She reached out a hand to tidy Melanie, but the child squirmed away self-consciously.

When they were inside the house, Giles said, "Go into the kitchen, kids, and ask Rae to give you some milk. I want a word with your mother."

Rac shepherded the children into the kitchen and shut the door behind her. Even so, she could hear the hum of voices and detect that Belinda's had acquired an angry note.

After ten minutes, the door opened and Giles came into the kitchen.

"Time to go, kids," he said.

They got down from their chairs. James bid Rae a polite goodbye, but Melanie asked brightly, "Will you be here next time?"

"Of course she will," said Giles before Rae could answer. "She's planning a surprise for you."

"Oh, what?" chorused both children.

"If I told you that, it wouldn't be a surprise," said Rae at once.

She followed them out into the hall where Belinda was waiting. Her cheeks were flushed and she gave Rae a sharp glance, but she said nothing beyond bidding her a frosty farewell.

When they were alone, Giles looked at Rae and said, "I did it."

"You're going to fight her?"

"I've already fought and won. You were perfectly right. She was bluffing. As soon as she knew I was prepared to fight for my right to be a father to my own children, she gave in."

"Giles, that's wonderful! I'm so glad for you."

"I don't know what to say to you, Rae. If it wasn't for you, I'd have lost that round and, as you said, it would have been the beginning of a slippery slope."

"But you won—that's what counts. Why did she look daggers at me?"

"Because I took a much firmer line this evening than I did when she and I talked this morning. It wasn't hard for her to work out where I got my courage from. I'm sorry I railroaded you into coming next time, but I was desperate. Her next trick is to try to persuade them that they don't really like visiting me, after all."

"Yes, I heard her just before she left this morning. It's all right. I'll gladly be here if it'll help."

"It'll do more than help. It'll make all the difference. On my own, I'm no match for Belinda. With you, I can stop her cutting me out of my children's lives."

"I'll do anything I can for you, Giles," she said quietly.

He looked at her eagerly. He seemed on the verge of saying something, and she held her breath. But he only laughed awkwardly and said, "That's settled, then. You're coming. Why don't we have something to eat?"

The low buzz in the courtroom increased in intensity as the door opened to admit the jury, returning with their verdict. Giles cast his client a look of reassurance. After Judge Lorrimer's summing up, Giles was reasonably sure of an acquittal.

As he returned to his seat, a clerk approached him and said in a low voice, "The judge's compliments, sir, and would you care to have lunch with him?"

Giles returned a polite message of acceptance, and when Judge Lorrimer returned he gave a brief bow of acknowledgment. The jury pronounced the defendant not guilty, and within twenty minutes Giles was on his way to the judge's room at the rear of the court. He wasn't surprised by the invitation, which was a common enough courtesy to a man who'd just taken an important step up. He read into it no more than that. Afterward he was to wonder how he could have been so naïve.

For most of the meal they talked shop. Judge Lorrimer was in love with his job, and now that he was on the verge of retiring he liked nothing better than to reminisce about old cases. Giles listened, genuinely fascinated, for the old man was a splendid talker. He was taken completely off guard when the judge said, "By the way, did you ever hear how much they made at that benefit dinner?"

"I heard it was substantial."

The judge told him the sum. "The charity was very pleased, though I must say, their thanks made me feel rather guilty. A bit much, being thanked when all you've done is enjoy yourself, don't you think? Not that you enjoyed yourself very much, I suppose."

"These things happen," said Giles cautiously. "It's all over now."

"Yes, of course it is. And since it is over, you won't mind if I tell you something about that business that always puzzled me?"

"By all means," said Giles politely. There was nothing else to say.

"I sat by that young woman almost the whole evening, and I'm dashed if I know how she got drunk when she never touched anything stronger than mineral water."

Giles drew in his breath slowly, calling himself a fool for imagining that he'd been invited merely to have lunch with a friendly old man. Since he'd sat down, this pit had been waiting to open at his feet.

Judge Lorimer's eyes were very bright as they looked at him. They were shrewd, too, Giles realized. He decided to risk some part of the truth. The old boy was smart enough to see through any lie.

"The fact is, she wasn't drunk," he said.

"That's what I thought. She must have had quite a grudge against you."

"I once prosecuted her father. She...didn't feel I'd been very fair. But I'm afraid I can't tell you who her father was. That's her secret."

"Not if she's going to show herself around the courts it isn't. There are plenty of people who saw her at Andrew Haines's trial, and then again in the lobby not so long ago. She's changed but she's still recognizable."

Giles swore. "If Bland—"

"It wasn't Bland. If you want to know, it was Craxton. You can imagine what he made of the fact that you're still seeing her. Don't look at me like that. The bar's the biggest gossip factory in the world, and you know it. If you will be seen with the daughter of a convicted criminal you must expect the worst. He got ten years, didn't he?"

"Yes, but he died after three months," said Giles harshly. His eyes had suddenly become shadowed as if with pain.

"And she blames you for his death?"

"She's never said that...."

Giles hesitated. "Don't tell me you blame yourself," said the judge. Then, when Giles didn't answer, he went on bluntly, "Don't be a fool, boy. You can't be answerable for what happens to people after the trial."

"I know that. I just wish he hadn't died."

"Nor are you answerable for what happens to a crook's daughter. I thought you had more sense."

"That evening I didn't know who she was."

"But you've discovered since that she's Tanis Haines. And you're still seeing her."

"She is not Tanis Haines," said Gilcs girmly. "She is Rae Bonham. She's put all that behind her. For God's sake, she's entitled to lead her own life!"

The judge looked at him with pity.

"You're the last man alive I ever thought to see making a fool of himself in this particular way," he said at last. "A little bit of fun on the side is one thing, but being seen in public with her, at a ceremony like that—"

"Judge, I have the greatest respect for you, but I must ask you to be careful how you speak of my friends," said Giles in a voice that had a dangerous edge. "Once and for all I want it plainly understood that Rae Bonham *is not a little bit of fun on the side*."

"Then I'm very sorry to hear it," said Judge Lorrimer after a silence.

They continued their meal awkwardly for a few minutes. Giles was wondering how soon he could decently leave.

"Are you thinking of marriage?" the judge demanded crisply.

"I don't know." Giles's expression discouraged further questions, but the old man wasn't deterred.

"I always understood that nothing but the top would do for you," he said. "Perhaps I was wrong about that."

"You weren't wrong," said Giles shortly.

"Then for pity's sake, what do you think you're playing at? Do you think you'll be made a judge if you're married to a crook's daughter? We're not talking about a minor conviction for petty theft. We're talking about massive fraud and a ten-year sentence. Are you under the impression that the whole world won't know?"

"The whole world seems to know now," Giles snapped.

"Give up this business while there's still time. Otherwise, Blake, I tell you frankly, you're facing a blank wall. You've made the step up to QC, and you're still flying high from the euphoria of that. I have no doubt you'll make a big success of it. Your clients won't care who you're married to as long as you win their cases.

"But that won't be enough forever. One day you'll have to face the fact that you've gone as far as you can go. And then you'll remember that you wanted to be a judge."

"But perhaps," said Giles quietly, "there are other things I want, too."

Judge Lorrimer snorted. "Rank sentimentalism! I never thought to hear that kind of talk from you."

"Neither did I," said Giles, more quietly still.

Spring moved into summer. Rae's final exams were approaching. Wrapped in study, she saw less of Giles, but she never missed the time they spent together every second weekend, when Melanie and James were there. As he'd predicted, her relationship with the children had flowered and their real enthusiasm for these weekends had defeated all Belinda's attempts to persuade them that they were unwilling.

For Rae, the real joy of these visits was their effect on Giles. Using her warmth as a bridge, he was gradually finding a way through to his children. He needed time, and it would always be hard for him to express his love for them, but even James was coming to understand that the love was there. Melanie seemed to have always known by instinct, and she made it easy for her father by going to meet him more than halfway.

Rae was happier now than she could ever remember being. There was a new freedom in being able to admit to herself that she loved Giles. When they were apart, she yearned for him. When they were together, she followed him with her eyes. The nights they spent in each other's arms were shaking in their loveliness.

It didn't trouble her that he spoke no words of love, and that gestures of affection came only with an effort. Sometimes their daytime relationship seemed no more than camaraderie. But against this she set the nights when she knew he was possessed by a passion as violent as her own. She couldn't believe that the need that drew him to her was merely physical. Once he'd allowed her to see the deep vein of untapped feeling in him, smothered below layers that the years and his wretched childhood had deposited over it, she had to find a way to bring it to the surface. Often she felt like a miner prospecting for gold who, knowing it was there, would be sometimes despondent but full of boundless joy when a fleeting glimpse renewed her faith. One day soon, she was sure, her moment would come.

One Saturday morning as they sat over breakfast, waiting for the children to arrive, Giles said, "This'll be the last time till your finals are over, won't it?"

"That's right."

"How do you think you'll do?"

"With reasonable luck, I think I'll do well. It's my own fault if I don't. Because of you I've had as much time as I need to work."

He made a gesture that dismissed this reference to his help.

"Look," he said, "if I'm not going to see you for a while, there's something I'd like to get settled now."

"Yes?"

He hesitated before saying, "Do you want some more coffee?"

"Yes, please."

He poured for her and replaced her cup. She sat waiting for whatever he wanted to say, but he seemed to be having difficulty finding the words.

"I'm having another battle with Belinda," he said at last. "A harder one this time. Now that the summer holidays are almost on us, I want to take the children abroad with me for a week. I need her consent and she's making difficulties. How will I manage to look after two children alone for a week—that sort of thing. I'm afraid I took the liberty of saying you'd be with us."

"That's all right. I'd love to come, as long as it's after my exams."

"Of course. The thing is, I want to take them to France." He poured himself another coffee, not looking at her. "Oddly enough, they're a bit straitlaced in the provinces. They'd get uptight about you and me not being married. They're probably right, too. It's about time we were thinking of it. It would make a lot of things easier."

She stared at him as his meaning gradually dawned on her.

"Just . . . what . . . would it make easier?" she said slowly.

"Well, it's obvious, isn't it? The kids think the world of you. When we're together, we feel like a family. If we really were one, well, I'd be in a far better position to stand up to Belinda if she starts her tricks."

"Yes," she said. "I can see that."

She thought, *Won't you tell me that you love me—if you do? I never doubted it till now.*

"Do you think that's a good enough reason to get married?" she said. "Just for the children?"

"Of course not, but . . . things are good between us, aren't they?"

"Yes . . ."

"I wouldn't get in the way of your career. Mrs. Jones runs the house. You could do whatever you wanted. What do you say?"

She played with her spoon, wondering if this was the great moment she'd waited for, dreamed of. Now she understood how much she'd counted on the hope that when it came, he'd wring the words out of himself, somehow. But the moment had come and it seemed that he couldn't.

"Have you really thought about this properly, Giles?" she said, playing for time, while confusion clamored within her.

"What do you mean?"

"I mean that you're a lawyer. My father was a convicted criminal. That's not going to do you any good if it gets out."

The silence made her look up. He had an expression she'd never seen before—wry, embarrassed, undecided, and suddenly she understood.

"Oh, dear God!" she exclaimed. "They already know."

"It doesn't matter," he said quickly.

"How did they find me out?"

"When you came to the court a few weeks ago you were recognized by people who'd seen you at Andrew's trial."

"I should have thought of that," she whispered in horror.

She'd thought of nothing, she remembered, but that she was going to see him again. That happiness had filled her, blotting out caution.

Tell me that you love me, that for you, too, nothing counted that day but to be together again.

"It doesn't matter," he said again. "It was bound to happen one day. Besides, I'm not ashamed of you. I'm not marrying you to hide you away."

She smiled faintly, "That's very chivalrous of you. But it isn't that simple, is it? You want to be a judge. They won't make you a judge if you're married to a convict's daughter."

"Will you stop calling yourself that?" he said angrily.

"It's what they'll call me. You have to face it. If you marry me, you won't be a judge. You know you won't."

Giles hesitated. Rae was too intelligent for a polite lie. It had to be honesty. But as so often before, his eloquence, so sharp and ready in court, was a blunt instrument in his private life.

"I don't know the answer to that," he said gruffly. "It'll be ten years at least before the subject comes up. Maybe the bar will be more sophisticated by then."

"And maybe pigs will fly. What would happen if you had to judge a case like my father's? The papers would have a field day: 'Mr. Justice Blake is peculiarly suited to understand the circumstances of this case as his own father-in-law did ten years for fraud and embezzlement—or would have if he'd lived.'"

Rae didn't see his look of pain. She was intent on driving her point home as hard as possible. Better for Giles to face the stark facts cruelly now than later, with bitter regrets.

"Marry me and you won't get the judgeship," she said flatly.

Say you love me. Say I matter more to you than any judgeship.

"Well, maybe I'm better off without it," he said. "I've been doing some thinking. I always wanted to be a judge, that's true. But I wanted it because it's the top of the tree, not because I was after the job for its own sake. In fact, my gift is for arguing. I'm an advocate by nature, and I'll probably be happier staying an advocate. A man should do what he's good at. I'd make a rotten judge, always wanting to stick my oar into the case I was trying."

"Or summing up in favor of the 'small, defenseless people' because you felt sorry for them," said Rae with a shaky smile.

"Exactly. All my judgments would be overturned on appeal. Nature meant me to be an advocate, Rae. It's no hardship to me to remain one. And for what it's worth, I'll earn ten times the money that I could as a judge."

It was all true, she knew. Giles would be a great advocate and earn a fortune. Looked at in a rational light, not being a judge was hardly even a sacrifice.

But you couldn't look at a man's lifetime dreams in a rational light. In ten years he'd be due for the next step up, a step his gifts would have earned for him. He'd be denied his dream at the very time when the children, for whose sake he'd married, were going out into the world to lead their own lives.

He'd know then that he'd made a sacrifice, one that only the deepest love could make bearable. Without that love, how soon would he look with bitterness at the wife who'd denied him what he most wanted?

Rae had always warned herself that she might have to take his feelings on trust. But suddenly the trust was no longer there. If his love wasn't great enough to wring some word out of him even at this crucial moment, neither was it great enough to endure the strains of the years to come.

She waited to be sure that Giles had nothing else to say before she spoke.

"It's nice of you to say that it doesn't matter," she said. "But I think it matters a lot. We'd better not get married, Giles. It's too risky. I can't let you give up what you've always wanted so badly, not . . . not when we have nothing going for us." To her own amazement, she got the words out sounding steady and cheerful.

Giles, too, looked cheerful as he considered this.

"I don't think you can say that we have nothing going for us," he began.

"Very little, then," she said quickly. "Not enough to take the chance. After all, it's not just your career, but mine, too. With any luck I'll be starting afresh in a demanding new job. That isn't the time to be taking on a husband. Let's leave it."

Giles was silent a long time. Years of professional training kept his face a blank mask that gave no hint of the storm of misery within. Passionate, pleading words—my love, my life, what will I do without you?—battered against his outer defenses, but could find no way to escape. At any moment it seemed that they must force their way out, but they were held back by chains of embarrassment and awkwardness that had been riveted into place too long ago to remember. *Acting silly!*

I love you, I love you. He heard the words in his head so loudly that it seemed that he must have said them, and was amazed to find that he hadn't. But at any moment they'd come pouring out and she'd realize the agony of love and desolation that she'd created inside him, even perhaps understand the terror that possessed him at the thought of losing her. He drew a deep breath and forced himself to speak.

"Well," he said, "that seems to be that."

Twelve

Three weeks later, Rae took her final exams. They were as tough as she'd feared, and she appreciated, as never before, the debt she owed to Giles. She knew now that without his help she'd have been too tired to do herself justice. As it was, her mind stood up well to the strain. She emerged after a few days, pale, worn out, but optimistic.

Despite their unwed status, they took the children and set off for France in a rented camper two weeks later. If all had been well with them, this would have been a blissful holiday. The sun shone all the time, Melanie and James enjoyed themselves and Giles had never been so at ease with his children.

But between himself and Rae the atmosphere was growing daily more strained. In part, this was because of physical circumstances. While they were living in a cramped camper with the two youngsters, the only relationship possible was platonic. The enforced abstinence made her more than ever aware of Giles's unmistakable masculinity, the size and power of his body. Memories of their lovemaking assailed her whenever she looked at him. She began to turn her eyes away whenever possible, realizing that he was doing the same.

But there was more than thwarted yearning to divide them. She knew that Giles was suffering because he found it hard to cope with rejection, but paradoxically she, too, felt rejected. She loved him. If he'd loved her, she'd have taken the risk of marrying him. Without love, the risk was too great.

She wondered how she could have ever deluded herself that he was in love with her. Because Giles found it hard to talk about his emotions, she'd filled up that gap with wishful thinking. But when the moment came, she'd had to face the emptiness that lay behind her dreams.

She began to see how their parting would come about. There'd be no scene or argument. They'd drift apart because they had nothing left to say to each other. Her pride wouldn't let her stay in his bed now that she knew his feelings were so much less than her own. From that moment on, she was saying goodbye to him in her mind.

Back in England, Giles had to depart almost immediately to take part in a conference that he'd agreed to months before. He was away for over a week, and by the time he returned Rae had received her results. They were first class.

As she felt the load fall from her shoulders, Rae waited for the surge of joy that she'd always known would possess her at this moment. But nothing happened. She saw only that she and Giles had reached the parting of the ways.

When she rang him with the news, he immediately suggested a dinner to celebrate.

"At the Ritz," he said. "Nothing but the best for your big night."

A punctilious escort, he picked her up dressed in dinner jacket and bow tie, just as he'd been on the night of their first meeting. Rae wore the elegant black dress she'd worn for Sam Rogers. She supposed it was inevitable that the two of them should dress up for the Ritz, but it served to underline the strange, artificial quality of this evening. She knew her sense of awkwardness was reflected in the way she accepted his congratulations, but she couldn't help it. There was no way she could feel natural with Giles tonight, and he, too, seemed constrained.

He knows, she thought, that we're saying goodbye because there's nothing else to say.

"How did your conference go?" she said when they were eating their starters.

The conference accounted for the next half hour. Giles talked with great perseverance, and by the time he ran out of things to say, they were in the middle of the main course. Rae hardly heard anything. She was watching him, storing up memories of his austere good looks, the graceful movements of his hands, the expression in his dark eyes.

"Kinroy finally finished the extension," he said as the plates were being cleared.

"What are you going to do with it?"

He suppressed a desire to say, Knock the damn thing down, and said instead, "Turn it into a place for my films."

If Giles could be said to have any kind of hobby it was old films, which he collected on video. Rae knew that when he worked on a case late into the night he often found it impossible to go straight to sleep. He'd unwind by putting on a cassette. Now, with an almost visible sense of relief, he began telling her about a new system of video projection he'd discovered.

"It projects outward, rather like a movie projector, and the picture goes onto a wall-size screen," he said. "So you need a big room. It'll be like having my own movie theater."

He talked for twenty minutes on this safe subject, unaware that what he was really making her see was the picture of himself alone in that great house, watching shadows.

"I've got two interviews next week," she told him when they'd ordered dessert, "both with good firms. One of them wrote me a letter saying my 'outstanding qualifications' made me a likely candidate for the vacancy. You were right about that. Thank you, Giles. I couldn't have got this far on my own."

He made a gesture of dismissal.

"You did it," he said. "I just came in at the end. You put in those years of work first—that, plus your brilliant mind. Do either of the jobs appeal to you?"

This subject carried them through the next half hour. Then she said, "I'll be able to support myself when I've got a job."

"There's no hurry for that. Don't take something that isn't right for you just to save me money. Make sure they pay you properly so that you can get out of that dreadful apartment. And if you can't get decent terms, turn them down. There are people I could introduce you to—"

"No." She interrupted him more sharply than she'd intended. "No, thank you, Giles," she said firmly. "I've accepted enough help from you. The bird's got to fly from the nest some time."

"I see," he said heavily. "You're right, of course." In a dispirited voice he added, "Perhaps it's time we had the champagne."

The waiter brought the champagne and opened it for them. When they were alone again, Giles lifted his glass to her. He was smiling, but suddenly she noticed how tired he looked. The conference must have worn him out more than he'd said, she thought.

"Here's to you," he said. "Be happy, Rae. Have everything you want out of life. That's my wish for you."

She smiled and raised her glass to him.

"I want the same for you too, Giles—have everything you want out of life."

She had the feeling that the heaviness in his manner became more pronounced than before.

"There's one thing I want," he said, "that I don't think I'll ever have now."

"What's that?" She held her breath.

"An easy conscience," he said quietly.

"But, Giles—if you mean Andrew—I thought we settled that. I haven't held anything against you for a long time, didn't you know?"

"I'm not talking about what happened in the witness box, Rae. I mean his death."

She stared at him. Never before had he given her the remotest idea that Andrew's death troubled him.

"But you weren't responsible for his death," she said.

"That's what I tell myself. A lawyer can't be responsible for what happens to people after the trial. That's one of the first things you learn. When the verdict's in, you put the whole thing out of your head. Only... I can't.

"I told you once that you haunted me, and so has he. I just wish he hadn't died so soon. Three months is such a little time. How do I know what killed him? You've said often enough that I savaged him in the witness box, and that I gave him another two years on his sentence. Perhaps if I'd gone easier, or if he hadn't had to face such a long sentence—I don't know. And I never will know. That's the worst thing of all."

"Giles, Andrew had a bad heart. He wouldn't have lived long, in any case. It wasn't your fault."

He gave a faint, unconvinced smile. "It's nice of you to say that, Rae, just as it was nice of you never to throw his death in my face. If you only knew how easily you could have destroyed me by doing so—"

"But I'm not being nice," she interrupted him eagerly. "Honestly, Giles, Andrew had a bad heart. He'd had a massive heart attack five years earlier, but he'd refused to take proper care of himself afterward. That was why he had another. It had nothing to do with you."

"Rae, please, there's no need for this—"

"You don't believe me? But *why*?"

"Perhaps because I want so much to believe you," he said wryly. "It seems to me that if this was true you'd have said something before now. I can't bring myself to believe in a comforting explanation that only emerges at this moment."

"I haven't said anything before now because I didn't know this worried you. *You* never said anything before now."

"If you want the truth, I didn't dare. It's a subject that fills me with horror."

"There's no need, I promise you."

"I want to believe you. If only there was some kind of proof."

"Damn proof!" she said angrily. "Stop talking like a lawyer."

"Unfortunately, the habit clings. Lawyers find it easier to believe when there's some sort of evidence. I'm afraid you're just being kind."

"When have I ever been kind to you?" she demanded. "I once hated you for what you did to us in the witness box, but I've never blamed you for Andrew's death. Doesn't that tell its own story? Do you think I'd have spared you? Isn't that evidence?"

"Of a sort, yes." But he still looked unhappy.

"What more do you want?" she pleaded.

"I don't really know. I just like evidence to be a bit more solid than that, especially from you."

"Why from me especially?"

"Because you've always been my accuser. Being forgiven isn't the same as being found not guilty. I'm sorry, Rae. I should never have brought it up. It's just that tonight I have a feeling that I want to tie up ends— No, that's not exactly it. I can't put it into words, but perhaps you know what I mean."

Looking at him in anguish, Rae knew exactly what he meant.

After that, the evening faded away. They were polite and pleasant to each other, but the silent spaces echoed between them, and it was no surprise to Giles when Rae said, "I ought to be getting along now. I need an early night." It was barely ten o'clock.

She let him drive her home but didn't invite him upstairs. She seemed in a hurry to get out of the car, and he, taking his cue from this, bade her a polite farewell and drove away.

If Giles could have seen what happened when she was inside her own front door, he'd scarcely have believed his eyes. First Rae took off the black dress and her slip and put them away. In their place she threw on a pair of scruffy old jeans and an even scruffier shirt. They were clothes to get dirty in, and she knew she was going to get very dirty.

Next she opened the door of what the Housing Department had grandly referred to as "the second bedroom," but that was about six feet by seven. She used it as a junk closet and never went in there.

Her heart nearly failed her at the sight of the room, full of suitcases and old boxes, all covered in dust. But she pulled herself together and began methodically taking the boxes out and placing them on her front room floor. One by one, she tipped the contents out onto the carpet and began frantically scrabbling through them. There were eight boxes altogether, and none of them yielded anything.

Refusing to be disheartened, she packed them all away and dragged out the suitcases. There were four of them, and she went through them all with a fine-tooth comb. As she worked, she sent up desperate, pleading prayers, for nothing in her life had been as important as this search. In the last suitcase she found what she wanted.

At once she grabbed the phone and called a cab. Only after that did she notice that it was three in the morning. She hesitated, wondering whether to put it off till tomorrow. But her heart told her that it must be done tonight, even if it meant getting him out of bed.

While she waited for the cab, she went to scrub the dirt from her hands. In the bathroom, she caught a proper look at herself, a ragamuffin whose dirty, streaky face perfectly matched her clothes. She began to run some water into the basin, but immediately there was a faint toot from outside. Hastily she passed a towel across her face, grabbed her coat and ran.

She'd said she was ready to get Giles up, but it wasn't really a surprise to see his downstairs light still on. She told the cab driver to wait for her and hurried onto the porch where she began to ring the bell urgently. He came to the door almost at once.

"Who . . . ? *Rae!* Good grief, what's happened to you?"

She went past him into the living room. A mirror on the wall gave her a passing glimpse of her disheveled appearance, but she forgot it at once. Her hand was clenched on something that she drew from her coat pocket.

"I thought you'd still be up," she said, "and I wanted you to see this at once." She held out her hand. "It's the evidence you wanted."

"What . . . ?"

"I didn't mention it over dinner because I wasn't sure I still had it. It's taken me all this time to find it, and I had to turn out every piece of old junk I had. That's why I'm in such a state. Well, go on, look at it...." He was staring at the thing she'd handed him as if turned to stone.

"It's a letter from Andrew's doctor," she went on. "He wrote to me two weeks after Andrew died. He told me something I hadn't known till then."

As if in a daze, Giles sat down and took the letter from its envelope. He spread the sheet with difficulty because the years had treated it badly and it was in poor shape. But he could make out the imposing Harley Street address, the date, eight years earlier, and the words below.

> I strongly advised Andrew to tell you everything before, but he was adamant that you should know nothing. You were thirteen when he had his first heart attack, and it happened while you were staying with some friends in France, so it was easy to hide it from you.
>
> Perhaps you remember coming home and finding him in hospital? The official story was a stomach operation, so that the financial press didn't get wind of what was up. Andrew insisted that you should believe that, too. The truth was a massive heart attack, which he only survived by the skin of his teeth.
>
> After that, I warned him many times that he wasn't leading a suitable life for a man in his condition, but he wouldn't listen. He loved being with you. He couldn't bear the thought of living like an invalid because either the two of you would be together less, or you'd tie yourself to his sickbed. Also, I think he believed he'd go on forever, whatever I said. But he'd tired himself so completely by then that it's inconceivable to me that he could have lived longer than a year, even if there had been no trial.
>
> So you see, my dear, you have no cause for bitterness. Andrew chose his own way....

Rae went and knelt beside Giles. "It's real," she said gently. "I didn't fake it or anything. I couldn't have. Look at the mess it's in. The damp got into it a bit. So it wasn't your fault, and you can be easy now. Giles—" He gave no sign of hearing her.

"This was why you hurried home?" he said slowly.

"Yes, I wanted to start hunting for it."

For the first time he seemed to take in her appearance.

"And you've been doing that all this time?"

"I turned out my junk room. That's why I'm in such a state. I suppose I ought to have tidied up before I came here, but I wanted you to see it at once."

He looked at her, puzzled. "You did this for me?"

She colored. "Yes. I wanted you to understand that everything's all right. You can keep it, if you like. If you ever have doubts, you can read it again." She stood up and gave an awkward laugh. Nothing was happening as she'd pictured it. Giles wasn't transported with joy. It was almost as though her care for him was an embarrassment. She felt gauche and out of place, and suddenly she couldn't wait to get out and never come back.

"Well, I'd better be going now," she said. "The cab's waiting outside. Goodbye."

She hurried the last word out huskily before her throat tightened too much to speak. She turned quickly and left him without another look. In the hall, she opened the front door and turned on the step to close it behind her.

"No!"

The sound froze her blood. It was like an animal in agony. Before she could move it came again, from the room she'd just left.

"Rae! Don't leave me!"

She was through the door in a moment, across the hall, into the room. Giles had risen to his feet and was standing, his eyes fixed on the door in terrible fear. When he saw her, he opened his arms and she ran to him. They closed around her like a steel vise, promising no escape.

"Don't leave me!" he said into her hair. *"I love you. Don't leave me!"* His arms tightened even more.

Crushed, gasping, she managed to stammer out the words he wanted to hear. He made her say them again and again.

"I won't leave you, Giles. I won't leave you—" His mouth cut off the rest. It was a harsh kiss, almost cruel in its desperate plea for reassurance. She put everything she had into returning it.

"I love you," he said again. "Rae, I love you, I love you." The words that had come with such difficulty he now said again and again, as though, having once breached the dam, the river poured forth in a torrent.

"Why didn't you tell me that when you asked me to marry you?" she said.

"I *couldn't*!" he said violently. "I tried. I thought you understood. Then I thought you didn't love me, but tonight you went home and hunted for that thing just to make me happy. I couldn't believe it, but then you went and I knew it would be forever."

"I thought you didn't want me."

"I want you always. You mustn't leave me. I won't let you." He buried his face against her once more, but she heard the muffled words, "We're getting married, do you hear?"

"You'll never be a judge."

"To hell with that!" he said, drawing away to look at her. "I'd make a lousy judge. I told you what I thought about that before."

"Mmm. But I thought you were just rationalising. You have to be sure, Giles. There are still going to be times when you mind."

"Yes, I know that," he said seriously. "But not half as much as I'd mind losing you. It's very simple, Rae. I can live without being a judge. I can't live without you." He searched her face anxiously. "Tell me that you love me—if you do."

"If...?"

"I've tried to believe it, but you never said anything—except just once you hinted something by accident. When you thought I was going away, you said you minded. If you knew how I built on that. I examined every word you said under a microscope, trying to make them mean what I wanted. You'd have laughed if you'd seen inside my head."

"Darling, I love you. But you made it sound as if you only wanted to marry me because of your children. I couldn't say yes."

"I was curled up inside. It was all I could think of to say. But you know what I'm like. I did my best. I know it wasn't very good."

She must take him as he was, a man who loved her more than his dream, but would always need her help to emerge from the cave where his shy, uneasy spirit lived. She kissed him tenderly.

The sound of someone clearing his throat significantly made them both look round.

"You left the front door open," said the minicab driver. "I wasn't sure if you were coming back."

"Heavens!" said Rae guiltily. "I'd forgotten about you. I'm terribly sorry."

"Do you want me to take you home now?"

"No, thank you," she said contentedly. "I'm already home. How much do I owe you?"

When the driver had gone they looked at each other.

"Do you really mean that?" said Giles, "about being home?"

"Wherever you are is my home," she said softly and went into his arms.

After a long time she said, "Do you know what I want more than anything else in the world this minute?"

"I hope I do."

"No, before that. I want a shower. I'm filthy."

"I'll help you."

He got into the shower with her and soaped her down. Worn out with her exertions, she put her arms around him and let him do most of the work, which he didn't seem to mind. When he'd dried himself and her, he took her to bed and loved her with all the passionate tenderness for which he could find no words. She seemed to understand, for as the first light of dawn crept into the room, she curled up in his arms and began to slide into a blissful sleep. Observing this, he bent his head to kiss her as gently as he had once before, and whisper words that he could never have said to her when she was awake.

But she wasn't asleep, not quite. She felt the kiss and heard the words and knew they were real. She remembered the other time, when she'd dreamed a dream so shakingly lovely that the memory of it had made her want to weep. Perhaps it hadn't been a dream, after all. She must ask him about it. Not now, but one day, a long, long time in the future. . . .

COMING NEXT MONTH

TO MEET AGAIN
Lass Small

Tanner. His name still sent her blood pounding. He had been Indiana University's heartthrob, but Laura had been too young and afraid of the look in his eyes to give him a chance. Yet his kiss still burned — should she chase old dreams?

BROOKE'S CHANCE
Robin Elliott

A silly bet had landed Brooke on the lap of the sexiest Santa in town. Chance Tabor wasn't *really* Santa, he was tall, dark, blatantly masculine and he claimed he had fallen in love with Brooke. But Brooke had been hurt before... should she take the risk again?

A WINTER WOMAN
Dixie Browning

Banker Cordelia Richardson spent her days with the most successful men in business — but they left her cold. Then along came Cyrus Burrus, a half-naked handyman with a chest that inspired awe. Would he take the chill out of her heart?

Silhouette Desire

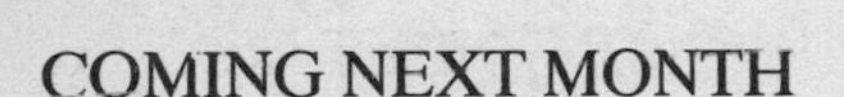

COMING NEXT MONTH

TOO HOT TO HANDLE
Elizabeth Lowell

Tory desperately needed the job she had been promised at Sundance Ranch. She arrived with only her suitcase and two dollars. She was not expecting to be greeted by the dark presence, cold eyes and explosive temper of Ethan Reever, the owner. How would she cope?

LADY LIBERTY
Naomi Horton

Genevieve was in a desperate hurry when a harmless highway flirtation with a sexy motorcyclist ended in disaster. But running into Griff had some advantages; she needed help and Griff was willing to supply it — at a price!

A FAIR BREEZE
Ann Hurley

Leah had come to Fairharbor to relax, when she wasn't scouring the area for artisans. Jonathon Wardell was one of those artisans, but he wasn't interested in selling his work. So Leah decided to find out just what it was that *did* interest this infuriating man…

APRIL TITLES

COURTING TROUBLE
Janet Joyce

HEAT OF THE NIGHT
Annette Broadrick

FOXY LADY
Marie Nicole

A LUCKY STAR
Jacqueline Jade

MY ONLY LOVE, MY ONLY HATE
Lucy Gordon

HANK'S WOMAN
Jo Ann Algermissen